DO.IN

This is a form of self-massage which combines with yoga techniques to revive and regenerate the body, harmonizing all levels of being – physical, psychological and spiritual – with the rhythm of life.

GW00394439

DO.IN

Eastern massage and yoga techniques

by

JEAN ROFIDAL

Translated from the French by Transcript

THORSONS PUBLISHERS LIMITED
Wellingborough, Northamptonshire

First published in France as *Do.In*
© Editions du Signal — René Gaillard — Lausanne, 1978
First published in England 1981
Second Impression 1982

© THORSONS PUBLISHERS 1981

British Library Cataloguing in Publication Data

Rofidal, Jean
   Do-In.
   1. Massage
   I. Title
   615'.822   RM721

   ISBN 0-7225-0651-1

Photoset by
Specialised Offset Services Limited, Liverpool
Printed and bound in Great Britain by
Whitstable Litho Ltd., Whitstable, Kent

CONTENTS

I dedicate this book to Georges Ohsawa, thanks to whom I received some marvellous instruction in the Yin-Yang principle.

PREFACE

I owe my development to Master Masahiro Oki whose pupil I had the good fortune to be and in whose dojo I got to know the oriental methods of physical treatment and met Japanese experts in *shiatsu*, Do-in and massage, who generously imparted to me everything they could of their experience. This information was given to me direct by actual practice, without words or books. It was only subsequently, when the practice had been acquired that I was permitted to gather documentary evidence and to supplement my knowledge, but the essentials were discovered through my body. In recognition of this I have, since 1971, devoted myself to this direct method of teaching by actual practice. However, yielding to the pressure put on me by numerous friends, I have now decided to spread the information more widely.

Ideally, I should like to have made a film showing the manipulations, but the theoretical part would have been missing. Background knowledge is indispensable, and the use of film poses practical problems. The solution, therefore, was to write a book in which the film is replaced by a complete and precise description of the manipulations. I would ask students to bear with me over the length of the text, as the fuller and more accurate the descriptions are the sooner they will be able to acquire the correct technique and to forget the book.

Speaking for myself, I owe my discoveries, made on the basis of the information imparted to me, to daily practice and research.

PART ONE

ENERGY AND DO-IN

MAN IS ENERGY

Like everything else, man is a manifestation of Universal Energy, having a very condensed centre (Yang), and a progressive expansion towards the periphery (Yin) which finally passes beyond the reach of our senses and of our measuring equipment. Our organs, that we choose to call material simply because we can touch, see and weigh them, extend into nerves which carry currents of nervous energy. Now, there is another form of energy not unlike nervous energy but even more subtle. This energy is only just becoming known to Western medicine through our growing understanding of Chinese acupuncture. It flows along tracks or 'meridians' along the surface of the body each of which are associated with specific organs. This energy enters and leaves our bodies by numerous, antennae-like points linking us with our immediate environment, and with the whole cosmos out to infinity.

Radiating around the human body is an energy-field known as the aura. People with an ability to see the aura know that it is composed of energies corresponding to each part of the body and that when an organ is unwell there is a modification of the aura in the corresponding zone. The energy radiating from a person is not confined by the aura. Indeed, man is part of the Universal Energy-field.

At the centre our energy is very condensed, compact and heavy – becoming visible as bones and organs, but around this physical frame circulate nervous and pranic currents which orientals term *Ki*. The body in fact, has around it a kind of energy 'skin'. When our organs are in poor health or are not functioning harmoniously, this 'skin' looks, to the clairvoyant's eye, full of tangled fibres and bare patches, rather like an uncombed head of hair.

The art of Do-in consists of manipulations carried out at a distance from the body, and of palpation and massage designed to improve the condition of this energy 'skin', to 'groom', so to speak, its 'unkempt fibres' and to harmonize the circulation of energy on the surface and in the body. By acting on the circulation of the subtle energies one acts indirectly on the organs.

Hara, the Vital Centre of Man

It is also important to know that the energies of each part of the body circulate in a harmony which, in sum, forms a spiral centred on the hara, a vital centre in man that is situated a few centimetres below the navel. When the energies are in conflict their combined effect can be very weak, even if they are strong in themselves, and in such a case the individual will feel weary and lacking in strength. On the other hand, when all the energies, even if weak, are harmonized, the total effect can be very strong. Since the hara is the centre of this vital circulation it has a multiple role consisting of:

The centre of mechanical, visual, psychic and mental equilibration.

The centre of memory, of the impulses preceding thought, the memory of the body.

The centre of assimilation. The intestines are coiled around the hara like the inductive winding round an electro-magnet. The stronger the hara is, the stronger is the energy induced in the intestines. This energy is essential for biological transmutations occurring at this body level, especially the synthesis of haemoglobin. The same can be said of all the other functions, including elimination.

The practice of Do-in consists of three parts:

1. *The manipulations*, the aim of which is the satisfactory distribution of energy circulation, the reactivation of stagnant energy and the recharging of deficient zones.

2. *Prana and Ki intake* by respiration and the appropriate gestures in order to recharge the body. These intakes of energy are facilitated by the fact that Do-in increases the permeability of the 'antennal' points and of the meridians.

3. *Centring the energy in the hara.*

The Beneficial Effects of Do-in
Do-in:

Stimulates the life of the organs, and fortifies and harmonizes all the functions.

Prevents diseases by restoring to normality an organ that was growing weak or was not functioning in harmony with the natural equilibrium.

Has a diagnostic use. When an organ is functioning badly, the corresponding zones, meridians and points become painful and we are forewarned of the condition long before we are made aware of it by organic pain. Therefore it is an aid to preventive medicine.

The practice of Do-in brings about a more sensible approach to eating, weaning us from those foods that are harmful to our bodies, and improving assimilation so that we have to eat less. Consequently our organs are rested and strengthened. Assimilation absorbs less energy, the functions of elimination benefit and this accelerates the process of purifying the body. Since the body is less occupied in transmuting the terrestrial energy represented by solid food, it is in a better position to receive the other energies.

It is well known that overeating leads to difficult respiration, so the practice of Do-in helps respiration and the utilization of the inhaled air.

The other more subtle energies circulating in our bodies, which nourish our intuition, are equally well received. The result is a better balance of the body and of all the spiritual and mental functions, improved sensitivity, a development of the intuition and a greater capacity to give, to communicate, to feel and to understand.

The Theoretical Bases of the Manipulations

Before going into detail about the manipulations, let us look at the energy geography of the human body. Naturally, it is necessary to talk about the meridians, but remember that they represent only one scheme of the circulation of energy in the body. The truth of the matter is that energy circulates everywhere.

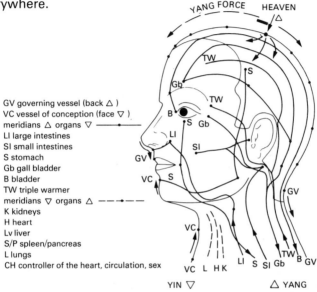

GV governing vessel (back △)
VC vessel of conception (face ▽)
meridians △ organs ▽ ———•———
LI large intestines
SI small intestines
S stomach
Gb gall bladder
B bladder
TW triple warmer
meridians ▽ organs △ ——•——
K kidneys
H heart
Lv liver
S/P spleen/pancreas
L lungs
CH controller of the heart, circulation, sex

Figure 1. The energy circuits of the head and neck.

In Do-in manipulations it is a good idea to massage the whole body. Do not confine treatment to the theoretical pathway of a meridian. Besides, the route taken by a meridian representing the main circulation of energy is not always exactly the same from person to person. That is why it is important to get the feel of the body first before going into details concerning meridians and acupuncture points.

The practice described in this book will allow the reader to perform Do-in for as long as he or she wishes without knowing anything about the meridians. It is hoped that the utmost importance is attached to this period so that sensitivity and our openness of mind can be developed allowing the energy to flow freely.

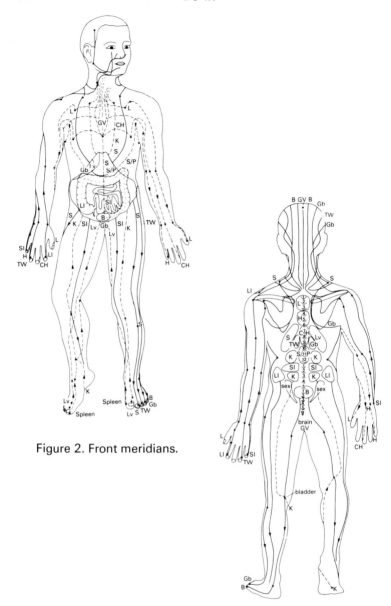

Figure 2. Front meridians.

Figure 3. Meridians of the back. Correspondence between the vertebrae and the organs and functions.

The Meridians
The parts of our body that are richest in 'antennae' and in meridians, and the most important ones for treatment purposes are the limbs and in particular the extremities: the hands and feet, then the wrists and ankles, then the fore-arms and lower legs, the elbows and the knees.

As an easy way of remembering how the energy circulates in the body, imagine someone standing with his arms raised. The person is represented by his vertebral column, which joins or 'yokes' heaven and earth (yoga = yoke), the legs and feet are the antennae directed towards the earth, while the head and arms represent the antennae turned towards heaven. It should be noted that the outsides of the arms and legs are harder than their insides; the former, covered with hair, are Yang; the latter, which are softer and more fragile, are Yin. The energy comes to us from the Heavens, the father, Yang,   , and from the earth, the mother, Yin,   ; two opposite and complementary roles. In Do-in one acts by following the meridians in the direction in which the energy flows.

Yin energy has its seat in the interior and Yang energy has its seat in the exterior. The Yang meridians are on the outside and the Yin meridians are on the inside.

The Yang energy from the heavens circulates along the backs of the hands towards the shoulders and from the hips towards the feet. The Yin energy rises up the inside of the legs and flows to the insides of the arms, from the shoulders to the hands. The Yang energy influences the Yin organs (intestines, stomach, bladder ... Yang meridians). The Yin energy influences the Yang organs (kidneys, heart, liver, spleen, pancreas ... Yin meridians).

The body has fourteen meridians: twelve paired meridians and two unpaired meridians on the front of the body (Yin) and in the back (Yang).

The meridians are shown in various sketches in this book. They are an approximation, a representation. There are very clear correspondences with all parts of the body even where only a few meridians are shown.

Do-in is not confined to treating the meridians, and to practice Do-in on the basis of knowledge of the meridians alone would be incomplete and artificial. For this reason, the different subtle correspondence between the whole body and one part of it are explained before any practical instructions are given for that part of the body. One must not lose sight of the spirit of Do-in. Everything is extremely complicated if one wants to analyse and document it, but the intuitive knowledge and practice of it are very simple.

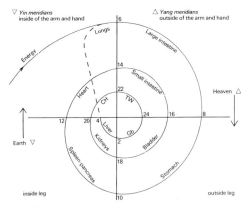

Figure 4. Circulation of energy along the meridians.

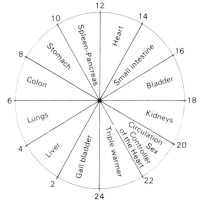

Figure 5. Chinese clock. Hours when energy fills particular organs.

Circulation of the energy
The energy circulates in the meridians and in the organs according to a certain daily rhythm. This harmony is illustrated in Figures 4 and 5.

PART TWO

THE PRACTICE OF DO-IN

FUNDAMENTALS

When

It is best to practice Do-in first thing in the morning before having anything to eat. By doing so the body is completely wakened and you will not suffer from the tiredness which sometimes seems to linger all day.

The entire body is then revitalized and ready to face the activities of the day. If you 'do not have the time' all you have to do is to rise an hour earlier, since the practice of Do-in will replace the lost sleep to good advantage. What is more, by practising Do-in every day you will gradually reduce your need for sleep. Six hour's sleep is enough, from 10 p.m. to 4 a.m., although this may be increased in winter to eight hour's sleep, from 10 p.m. to 6 a.m.

Through the year then, your hours of sleep can vary according to the season from six to eight hours, which is quite sufficient. If you eat once a day, four hour's sleep is sufficient, whereas if you eat three times a day you will need nine hour's sleep. Restrict your intake of food to two meals, one at noon and the other at 6 p.m.

The practice of Do-in leads progressively to the adoption of healthy rules of living. As your body is purified and your instinctive sensitivity is awakened, you will be surprised to find yourself questioning your way of life and, almost without noticing it, you will bring it into harmony with the Order of the Universe.

Where

When practising at home, always do so in the same place if

possible. Your body (by which is meant the whole man: body-spirit together with all the energy radiations) will grow accustomed to this place and will consequently be much more prepared to receive the benefits of Do-in. All you need do is to kneel down there to feel at ease and in harmony with your surroundings. When away from home, try to find a quiet well-ventilated spot, but do not be put off if this is not possible: Do-in can be adequately practised while travelling in an aeroplane or by train. It is most important, in fact, to practice Do-in when on a journey, because it will help you to adjust to the new environment and the cosmic equilibrium of the place you are in, and your understanding of the new surroundings and the people in them will thus develop more quickly and favourably.

Position

The best position is 'Seisa', the Japanese way of sitting, with the lower legs folded under the thighs, the big toes crossed and the heels on each side of your bottom (Figure 6).

To discover the best spacing between the knees once you are in the sitting position, rock slightly backwards and forwards one to three times while slightly raising the bended legs; the lifted knees will then return to the floor the right distance apart. This distance is different according to the individual concerned and according to the day, the time of day and the state of the digestive organs.

The Seisa position is excellent because it puts pressure on the meridians and points situated in the legs and 'yangizes' the corresponding organs. If you are unable to adopt it, it is a sign that you have too much water in your legs, that your organs are too Yin and that you eat too much. This position of the legs and pelvis allows you to keep the spine perfectly straight with the head directly above it, and to superimpose, one above the other, the three vital centres of the body, just as they should be: the hara, the heart centre and the mesencephalon, which are joined by the spiritual channel.

In this position, which is that of Zazen meditation, the energy circulates well along the spinal column and flows evenly on each side. According to circumstances, you can practise with the breath descending to the hara or rising towards the mesencephalon (Yang or Yin). When the aim of Do-in practice is physical and therapeutic, as in this book, we would recommend respiration in the hara as for Zazen meditation. If this position becomes uncomfortable, you can sit cross-legged. Do-in may also be performed while standing, while sitting on a chair or, if one is ill, while lying down. You can also perform it on someone who is unwell in order to revitalize them.

The Order of Practice
It is very important to perform Do-in manipulations in the order described in this book. Moving about without rhyme or reason from one part of the body to the other is quite wrong, and can leave you in a state of nervous irritation.

The Intensity of Do-in
If you are tired, perform a light Do-in, by passes on the surface of the body, and by using light manipulations, pressing and tapping.

If, on the other hand, you feel full of energy, perform a vigorous Do-in.

Preparations For a Do-in Session

Zazen Meditation (Figure 6)

Figure 6.

1. Sit in the Seisa position, placing the hands on top of the thighs against the lower abdomen with the palms turned upward, the left hand resting in the right hand and the thumbs held horizontally with their tips touching.

2. Direct the gaze to a spot about six feet on the floor in front of you.

3. Keep the back straight but relaxed.

4. Breath calmly.

5. Maintain this position for a few moments.

Figure 7.

Respiration (Figure 7)

1. Starting from the Seisa position, place the hands on the thighs.

2. Slide the left hand onto the floor in front of the left knee, then the right hand in front of the right knee, and join the hands by touching the tips of the thumb and index finger of one with the tips of the thumb and index finger of the other.

3. As the hands are slid forward in turn, breathe out gently and bend down until the chest rests on the

thighs. At the same time, keep the back as straight as possible with the nape of the neck in line with the back and the face over the hands. Remain in this position for a brief instant with the lungs empty, then sit up again while breathing in.

This salutary form of breathing repeated several times will, on the physical plane, give a good internal massage and make the back supple. It has other effects on the psychic and spiritual planes: it is part of prayer in all religions, humility, and the recognition of Mother Nature.

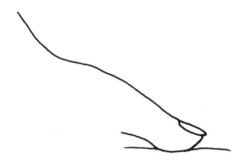

If you are practising Do-in in a group, this respiration-prayer made together will establish the harmony of the group.

Massage Technique

The massage is done mainly with the thumb-pad, the thumb being held perfectly straight (see diagram above and Figure 17).

When a point is painful and hard, for example the 'point of the intestines' between the thumb and the index finger (Figure 8), the massage is applied by turning the thumb without pressure while remaining within the limits of the pain. The pain subsides little by little as the area grows softer; so gentle pressure is applied until the pain returns and the treatment is continued as before. In this way, one nibbles away at the pain and the contracture.

There are several techniques for massaging a particular point and for exerting a specific action on a given organ. The best known are deep centrifugal massage in a spiral with the thumb generally held as explained above, performed to disperse the energy and to have a calming effect, and light centripetal massage in a spiral also performed with the thumb or preferably with the tips of the fingers for toning up.

When a point is particularly painful, it is best not to treat it directly. Instead, treatment should be carried out on its homologue on the opposite limb.

In order to facilitate the free flow of energy, it is best to remove any rings, necklaces, bracelets or watches before practising Do-in, because metals concentrate the energy.

THE HANDS

The hands of man are marvellous instruments and with them he can achieve anything. They set him apart from the animals. Your hands are going to be your tools in practising Do-in, and therefore special importance is attached to them. Together with the feet, they are the most significant centres of the meridians and antennae.

The meridians terminate at the tips of the fingers and the energy changes in polarity. Each finger is an antenna and an important pole. It is very beneficial for the whole body when they are lively, supple, and perfectly relaxed so that the energy can circulate well. Do not hesitate to exercise fingers, to 'crack' them and to warm them by massage in order to make them as supple as possible.

In every part of the body there are connections with all other parts, but certain parts link up more readily than others do with the sources of vital energy and with the organs. This is true of the hands and feet. If you have only a few minutes to spare, or if you are travelling as a passenger, do Do-in on your hands and you will find that you are entirely revitalized and refreshed.

The Healing Power of the Hands

The hands are the poles of our bodies. The right hand is Yang (positive), the left hand is Yin (negative). By placing our hands together we make one in ourselves; we cancel the duality of our body. This produces a mental calm and is the attitude adopted in prayer and meditation. A very important

Figure 8. The meridians and correspondences of the hands.
8a. Yang meridians △.
8b. Ying meridians ▽.
8c. The inside of the hand.
8d. The thumb and index finger.

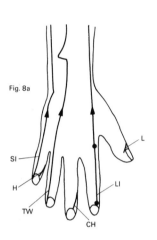

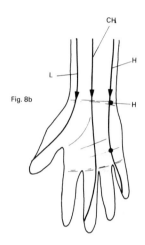

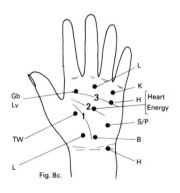

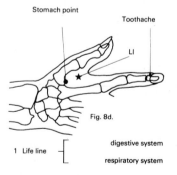

practice is to rub the hands together: the two opposite poles recharge themselves as in a magnet, the mind is set at rest and there is an improved energy flow in the body. We do it instinctively to give ourselves renewed courage to tackle a piece of work or when we are excited, impatient, worried or frustrated.

There are three main centres in the body: the hara, the heart and the mesencephalon and these radiate energies ranging from the most material (hara – Yang) to the most spiritual (mesencephalon – Yin). By rubbing the hands on the surface of the abdomen, the region of the heart or on top of the head, you can recharge yourself in different ways.

You can place your hands which have been charged in this way on yourself or on some other person, since they now possess healing power. It goes without saying that their effectiveness is a function of your state of health. If you wish to heal yourself or others by the laying on of hands it is desirable to do so when fasting. During digestion, the body turns in on itself and can only with difficulty give anything to the exterior. This marvellous power that the hands have will be fully utilized in Do-in.

The correspondence between the thumb and fingers and the organs
See Figure 8 for the meridians of subtle energy that pass through the fingers and for the various organs that they influence.

The thumb, through which runs the lung meridians, also corresponds to the liver. The liver and lungs are closely linked. Chronic bronchitis, with signs of pleurisy, which resists any direct treatment on the lungs, is often due to a poor liver function and when the liver is treated, the bronchitis disappears. Respiratory troubles (asthma for example) can be relieved by pressing hard on both sides of the thumbnail.

The forefinger, traversed by the meridian of the large intestine, corresponds to the function of assimilation. The tip of this finger is connected with the mouth and, in particular, there is an important point at the base of the nail on the outer edge. In the event of toothache, or if undergoing dental surgery without an anaesthetic, press hard on this point with the cutting edge of the thumbnail.

Then, running along the back of the hand, there is the meridian representing the whole digestive tract with the large intestine on the last phalange and in the fleshy part between the thumb and forefinger. The muscle here ought to be supple and elastic. If it is slack the intestines are loose (Yin); if it is hard and painful the intestines are congested.

The middle finger corresponds to the circulation of the blood. This is the first finger to turn white at the tip on a cold winter's day. It is traversed by the meridian known as the controller of the heart, which is also related to the circulation of the blood and sexuality.

The ring finger (significantly termed *medicinalis* in Latin) indicates the state of the nerves and the general state of health.

The little finger corresponds to sexuality. It is traversed by the meridians of the heart and of the small intestine. The function of sexuality is linked with the proper working of these two organs. If you turn to Figure 4 you will see how the circulation of the energy flows from one function to the other: heart ➔ small intestine ➔ bladder ➔ kidneys➔ controller of the heart, sexuality, circulation.

The two functions, those of the heart and the small intestine, are harmonized by taking the tip of the finger between the thumb and index finger of the other hand and by pressing on the nail. The effect is to encourage peristalsis in the intestines, and this acts beneficially in cases of constipation. Very hard pressure with the edge of the thumbnail of the other hand at the base of the nail on its inner side helps to relieve various heart troubles, such as palpitations.

The palm is another area rich in energy points (see Figure 8c) and it, too, has connections with all the organs of the body.

One special part is the centre of the palm. Traditionally, the hair of laziness is said to grow there! What is more to the point, if a hair really could grow there, even symbolically, it would do so because the palm was not being rubbed. In fact, if this zone is massaged our energies are revived. The evidence is to be seen in everyday habits:

> We rub our hands together briskly when working up the courage to tackle some job.

> We instinctively and without realizing it, rest the hollow of our hands on the top of some convenient tool-handle when pausing for a few moments to recoup our energies.

> When a walking stick is carried it presses into the hollow of the hand at every step. The effect of this is to keep us alert, which is more helpful than any mechanical support it may provide.

> An old country remedy for lazy children is to rub the palms of their hands with garlic to make them more active.

> A drop of cold liquid here is also helpful for palpitations, etc., or press the hollow of the left hand with the pad of the right thumb.

DO-IN ON THE HANDS

1. Sit up nice and straight, raise your arms horizontally in front of you, with your shoulders down and relaxed, bend your elbows and then grip the thumb of one hand on either side of the nail between the bent index finger and the thumb of the other hand, pressing hard (Figures 9 and 10).

2. Next exert pressure on the thumb by pushing it towards the palm and massage the whole thumb with a twisting motion, paying particular attention to each joint. Turn it, warm it and rub it.

Figure 9.

3. Finally, and always keeping the arms at shoulder
   level, give the thumb a pull while breathing out.

By twisting the thumb and turning it on its axis while
rubbing it in a spiral direction, you stimulate the
corresponding organ. The pressure exerted towards the hand
by pushing the thumb has the effect of inducing a
contraction in the corresponding organ — a 'yangization'. The

Figure 10.

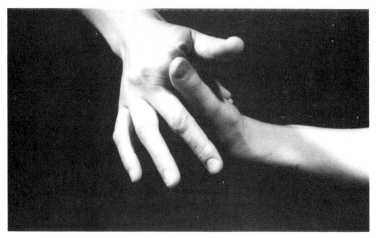

Figure 11.

final tug on the thumb opens out the joints between the phalanges, encouraging the energy to circulate better and relaxing the corresponding organ. At the end of treatment the finger should be left in a state of rest.

Figure 12.

4. Each finger should be treated in the same way, attention being paid to each joint and, in particular, to the one which attaches the finger to the palm.

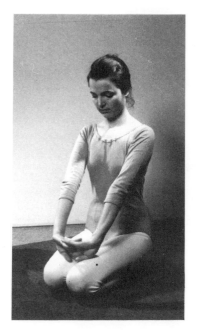

Figure 13.

Figure 14.

The finger should be rotated on this joint, first one way, then the other.

5. Massage and pinch the skin between the fingers where they meet the palm.

6. Then catch hold of each finger, one after the other, with the whole hand and bend them inwards until they make an angle of 90° with the palm, and

afterwards pull them back towards the back of the hand being treated (Figures 11 and 12)*

7. Do the same with the other hand.

8. Interlock the fingers and turn the palms to face away from the body; at the same time extend the arms palms down towards the hara. Breathe out while pushing with the arms to stretch the hands and repeat at least three times a day. This exercise opens and stretches the palm and fingers, and the effect of this is to relax the mind (Figure 13).

9. Keeping the fingers linked, turn the hands and arms in an upward direction and pull them forward as much as possible. This stretches the hands, wrists and forearms (see Figure 14).

Figure 15.

10. Still keeping the shoulders down and relaxed, lift up the arms in V-formation, breathe in deeply and imagine that the breath, carrying the energy or Ki, enters *via* the hands and descends along the arms and into the body.

*Never force the fingers or treat them roughly and if the hands are arthritic or infirm take medical advice before exercising them.

11. Lower the arms and clasp the palms of the hands together with a light pressure, holding them at the level of the hara, an inch-and-a-half or so in front of the abdomen. Then breathe out while imagining that the expiration descends back along the arms and leaves by the palms (Figures 15 and 16).

12. Repeat this intake of energy at least three times.

Figure 16.

Figure 17.

13. Taking this position as a starting point, hold the arms naturally low with the hands at hara level and perform a deep massage on the palms of each hand (Figure 17).

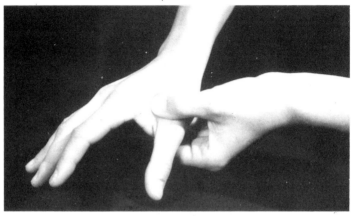

Figure 18.

14. Generally speaking, fleshy parts such as the palms should be given deep massage, whereas the skinny parts such as the back of the hand should be rubbed superficially.

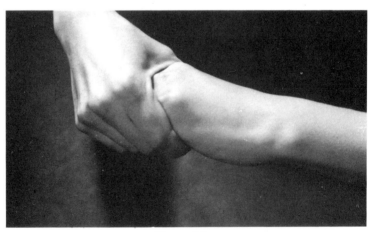

Figure 19.

15. Palm massage (for the main points see Figure 8c) should be continued down the insides of the fingers.

16. Give the same deep massage to the part situated on the back of the hand between the thumb and the index finger (intestines) (Figure 18), sliding along the inside edge of the thumb towards its tip (*liver*).

17. Then massage the backs of the fingers on re-ascending, and the backs of the hands in the same direction, lightly, sliding between the metacarpals (the bones between the wrist and the fingers).

18. Catch hold of the entire hand, with the back of the hand held crosswise in the palm of the other hand, and try to squeeze the metacarpals in order to make the back of the hand round and supple (Figure 19).

19. Knead the whole hand and fingers *ad lib* in order to empty them of blood and decongest them.

20. Rub the back of the hand to warm it up well and continue by sliding towards the wrist.

Figure 20.

THE WRISTS

The wrists should be very supple as this reflects essentially a satisfactory functioning of the heart and liver.

1. After the wrist has been well warmed up by rubbing, bend the wrist forwards and backwards thus stretching it both ways (Figures 20 and 21).

2. Poke into all the little hollows between the joints with the thumb all round the attachment to the hand. Search out all the little sore places which correspond to stagnant energy that disturbs the functioning of the corresponding organ — for example, heart and eyes on the internal edge (Figures 22 and 23).

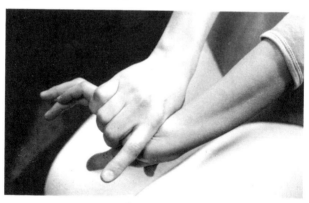

Figure 21.

Figure 22

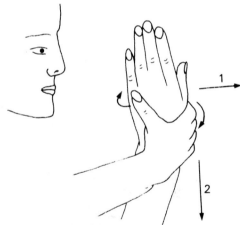

Figure 23.

3. Rotate the hands in both directions.

4. Raise the arms and shake the hands freely.

Warm up, stretch and turn all the joints of the hands, wrists, elbows and shoulders. This method deserves some attention and we hope it will be fully understood from the text and illustrations.

Figure 24.

1. Lift an open hand to the level of your face with the little finger facing your nose and the palm turned to the right in the case of the right hand and to the left in the case of the left hand.

Figure 25.

2. Place the thumb of the other hand behind the metacarpal of the little finger, with the palm on the back of the hand and the four fingers folded round the base of the thumb, on the corresponding metacarpal on the edge of the hand.

Figure 26.

3. Using the hand that is grasping the open hand, twist the latter as far as possible by pushing the little finger outwards — towards the right for the right hand (Figure 24).

Figure 27.

4. When the maximum torsion has been obtained and held at the limit of pain, the two arms are pushed forward and slightly up in order to transmit the

Figure 28.

torsion to the whole arm as far as the shoulder joint (Figure 25).

5. Breathe out when extending the arms and breathe in when bringing them back to position one.

6. Next, place the thumb of the working hand (Yang) behind the metacarpal of the ring finger of the hand undergoing torsion (Yin). Apply the maximum torsion and once more extend the arms while breathing out.

7. Do this behind each of the four fingers in turn.

8. Then hold the already treated arm straight out in front of the body in a horizontal position, turn the open hand with the thumb pointing downwards and the palm facing away from you (to the left in the case of the left hand – Figure 26), place the other (active Yang) hand on the back of the Yin hand with its palm on the back of the latter and its thumb hooked round the edge of the passive hand at the level of the metacarpal of the little finger (Figure 27).

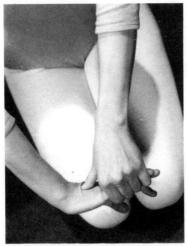

Figure 29.

9. Twist the passive hand as far as possible by turning its palm upwards, so as to twist the whole arm, right up to the shoulder.

10. Holding this position, bring the two hands towards the chin, while breathing out, keeping the elbows as low as possible (Figure 28).

11. Extend the arms while breathing in.

12. Repeat three times at least.

13. Warm up the wrist which has undergone the torsion.

14. Treat the other arm in the same way.

15. Resume your original position, with the open hand in front of your face and the thumb of the other hand applied to the middle of the back of the hand undergoing torsion.

16. Impose the torsion and, while preserving it, lower the hands vertically in front of the body while breathing out. Then raise them again while breathing in. Repeat this several times (Figure 29).

Continue by twisting in the opposite direction as follows:

17. Lower the passive arm and turn the palm of the hand to face the floor with its thumb towards your abdomen. Then place the thumb of the other hand on the back of the passive hand and hook your four fingers round the edge of the little finger. Press with the thumb and pull with the fingers to turn the passive hand forward. Breathe out when applying and breathe in when releasing the torsion. Repeat several times (Figure 30).

18. Rub and warm the back of the passive hand energetically, together with the wrist and elbow.

19. Go on to treat the other arm similarly.

Figure 30.

THE ARMS

The arms correspond to the voluntary part of the individual. For many of us, even though we are active and decisive, the arms are too contracted and there is an accompanying tension and anxiety. It is no longer the individual who takes his work in hand voluntarily, but the work which dominates and controls the individual. It is essential to relax the arm muscles in every possible way, to warm them, to knead them in depth, purge them of their stagnant blood, to fill them with fresh blood and replenish their energy or Ki. This is managed by the following practices:

Passes at a distance

1. Move your hand up the outside of the opposite arm without touching it, with the hand an inch away from the skin.

2. Describe a spiral over the shoulder joint.

3. Return above the inside of the arm.

4. Turn at the finger tips and move back up on the outside. Repeat the whole operation several times and then change over to the other arm.

It is also possible to move alternately several times from one arm to the other like this:

1. Move up the left arm with the right hand and descend on its inside.

2. Continue with the left hand by moving up the right arm and descending it on the inside.

3. Repeat with the right hand etc.

Friction

Act in the same way as before, but now make contact with the skin as strongly as you feel is necessary.

Massage

1. Massage along the meridians in the direction of the energy flow, that is to say, descend on the inside and ascend on the outside of the arm using the fleshy part of the thumb.

2. Look for the little sore spots in the elbow joints and disperse them.

3. Knead the muscles and bones.

4. Knead the deltoid muscle vigorously and squeeze it in your hand to empty it of blood.

The base of the deltoids is related to the nostrils on the corresponding sides and if there is something the matter with one of your nostrils, massage the base of the deltoid muscle on the same side and you will find a painful point there requiring treatment. The middle of the deltoid is related to the circulation of blood in the eyes.

5. Give the biceps deep massage to relax the arms (tones up the heart).

Tapping

With a very loose wrist and the hand half-closed, tap the back of the arm all the way up from the hand to the shoulder and then return down the inside, right to the palm and the insides of the fingers, which can be struck as the back of the hand is supported on the thigh.

Points in the arm requiring special treatment

1. On the inside surface of the forearm, pay special attention to massaging the controller of the heart meridian from the elbow to the wrist.

2. On the external edge of the forearm, between one and two inches below the elbow joint, there is an important point that is often painful when pressed. For this reason it should be very easy for you to discover it, but if you do not, so much the better, everything is going well and there is no need to worry about it.

   If the point is painful however and therefore easy to locate, massage by pressing-movements on the spot. This will improve the general condition, relieving nervous exhaustion and nervous tension, headaches and constipation.

3. There is another sensitive point on the outer side of the arm, in the centre between the biceps and the triceps and almost equidistant from the elbow and the shoulder. You can feel it roll under your finger like a grain of rice.

   This point should be treated if it is painful. It corresponds to a general build up of toxins in the body. Treating it is very effective in the case of food poisoning or insect bites.

4. There are numerous points in the fold of the elbow that correspond to the intestines, menstruation, fevers, etc. Look for sore spots as in the other joints and dissolve them. Each joint is a chakra, an important antenna, and also a zone of intersection, an energy relay; but blockages of energy occur in them which it is important to break down.

5. Generally speaking, the state of the arms (and of the legs too) affects the health of the eyes and ears.

THE DO-IN SEQUENCE

When the hands and arms have been thoroughly revived, warmed and revitalized and are permeable to the surrounding energy, the instruments are ready for an integral Do-in.

The Do-in sequence will be set out as follows:
— head
— face
— ears
— nape of the neck
— neck
— shoulders
— the awkward place between the shoulder blades
— chest
— respiration, prana intake
— body height
— feet
— legs
— pelvis
— kidneys – back
— abdomen
— massage while lying on the ground
— concentration in the hara
— stretching
— relaxation
— chants
— adjuncts (corrective exercises)

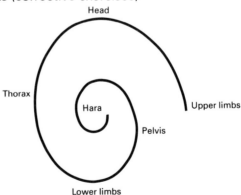

Figure 31. The Do-in sequence spiral.

THE HEAD

The way the organs are arranged in the body is mirrored in the arrangement of corresponding centres in the head.

That part of the forehead above the left eye corresponds to the stomach, then come the spleen and the pancreas and, over the right eye, the liver. The small intestine is coiled on the top of the head between the forehead and the crown, and the large intestine describes its spiral outside this (as in the abdomen) and ends at the anus on the crown itself. At the back, we find the kidneys, the urinary passages and the sexual organs (Figure 32a).

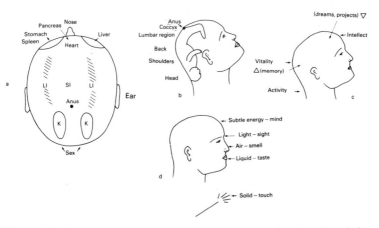

Figure 32. Correspondences between points on the head and the body functions.

The head has many correspondences of all kinds. To give another example, the entire structure of the spinal column is set out with all its parts on the back of the head as shown by the infant's body in Figure 32b. There are also relations there between its zones and the emotional, intellectual and psychic life of the individual (Figure 32c).

With the hand half-closed, tap the various zones from the stomach to the anus, following the course taken by the digestive tract; in the same way that the abdomen is massaged in the direction taken by the contents of that tract.

This tapping excites peristalsis of the intestines and, in particular, by tapping on the crown of the head, constipation and haemorrhoids are treated.

Then, using each fist, tap the zones representing the kidneys and continue tangentially from the base of the head and up to the crown.

Diagnosis

Do-in of the head provides a good means of diagnosis, because if one is suffering from a 'bad head' and if a zone is painful and cannot bear being tapped, the reason is that the corresponding organ has been taxed by a temporary excess of food or is on the verge of malfunctioning. It should not be forgotten that a pain in any point on the head is one of the body's danger signals and one should use this to identify the cause of the disorder and to bring one's habits more into line with natural laws.

Nevertheless, since re-education is not achieved over night, the first step is to treat the head pain and to keep it from disrupting normal activities (sleep, work etc.). Usually, the diet has been too rich or too Yin (distending the stomach as does sugar and alcohol), there has been prolonged exposure to the sun (its heat causes dilation), or nervous tension is causing constriction of the blood supply. All these things bring about a dilation of the tissues and a liquid increase that tends to build up pressure under the dome of the skull.

The main feature of the treatment is to apply pressure on the outside to counteract dilation on the inside — an instinctive reaction when one is in the grip of mental

Figure 33.

suffering, distraction or obsession. The corresponding centre is in the middle of the frontal zone under the hair (Figure 32c: the centre of dreams, projects, intellectual processes, nervous tensions and so on). This is sometimes painful when tapped, which is how the sufferer can locate it before treating it by applying pressure.

The simplest Do-in method to use is to keep the fist flexible at the wrist and to tap gently at first and then increasingly strongly until the limit of pain is reached.

There are also other ways of exerting pressure, for example:

1. Press with the finger-tips on either side of the median line of the head from the front to the crown (Figure 33).

2. In particular, treat in the same way two symmetrical points on the front of the head, at the intersection of the lines passing through the centre of the eyes and in front of the ears (Figure 34). At these points you will find two little hollows where the skull gives slighty under the pressure of the fingers. Press while breathing out and release the pressure while breathing in. This practice soothes migraines and nervous tension.

Figure 34.

Figure 35.

3. Press on your forehead with the palms of your hands and massage it spirally.

4. Rub your forehead from the centre to the temples and then move back along the temples to above the ears while pressing strongly, as if to tear the hair (Figure 35).

5. Press on the temples with the heels of the hands.

6. Warm the nape of the neck and massage its points of attachment to the head (see the section on Do-in of the nape of the neck).

Figure 36.

7. Dash very cold water over it and follow with an immediate energetic towelling (the cold tightens the tissues).

8. If you have a partner, the latter can soothe you by placing his or her left hand on your forehead and massaging the back of your head fairly strongly with the fingers of the right hand. It is also possible to practise this treatment on oneself.

9. A more precise method is to pinch the root of the nose between the thumb and index finger and to press strongly with the fingers on the back of the head (Figure 36), or into the hollows situated on either side of the cervical vertebrae under the bones of the head.

This treatment can also be given by a partner.

With the help of a partner, it is possible to act directly on the organ corresponding to the painful zone. For instance, if one of the kidney zones behind the head is painful, this indicates that the kidney is diseased, overworked, blocked or deficient. In this case, the subject lies stretched out prone with the arms folded and the hands under the face. If it is the right side that is painful, the patient raises the right leg and tenses it while his or her partner tries to resist this movement by pressing on the heel. The effect of this action is a powerful contraction of the whole mass of muscles supporting the kidney. The latter receives deep massage and the head pain usually disappears, showing that the kidney has greatly benefited from the treatment.

There are numerous techniques you can invent, but they all belong to one or other of the following three classes:

Direct action on the painful area in the head.

Action on the organ.

Removal of the cause of the trouble by finding the error committed (faulty feeding, overwork, bad posture, ill-fitting footwear, quarrels, stress etc.).

After performing Do-in on the head, rub the hands together (see the section on the healing power of the hands) and smooth or comb the hair as you please.

The Face
Before and during Do-in of the face, rub your hands together well in order to charge them, and do so as often as you feel the need.

The face – the eyebrows – the temples

1. Using the pads of the three main fingers (index to ring finger), massage the face in an upward direction above each eye (related to the bladder) then the sides of the face towards the top (along the gall bladder meridian).

2. Massage the area between the eyebrows. This centre is related to the nape of the neck. When the nape is stiff or tired (after a yoga head-stand for example) press strongly (Yang) on this point with the bent knuckle of the thumb, and the back of the

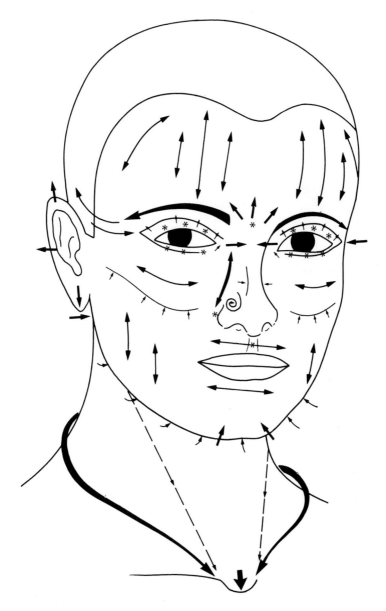

Figure 37. Do-in of the face and neck.

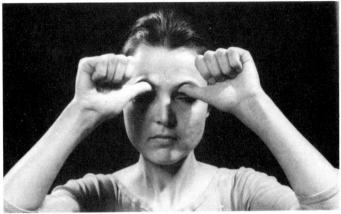

Figure 38.

neck will relax (Yin). This zone is also related to the liver, pancreas and spleen (Figures 37 to 40).

3. Stretch the eyebrows from the centre towards the temples. The stretching of the eyebrows (related to the shoulders) is also applied to the temples and round to the back of the head (gall bladder and meridian).

4. Massage under the superciliary arches with the ball of each thumb and locate any small sore spots in the bony notches (liver) between the nose and the outer extremities of the arch (Figure 38).

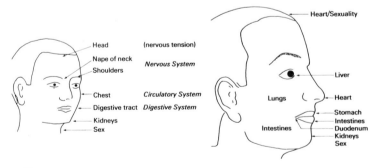

Figure 39. Correspondences of the various points of the face.

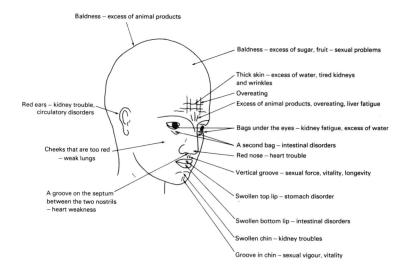

Baldness – excess of animal products

Baldness – excess of sugar, fruit – sexual problems

Thick skin – excess of water, tired kidneys and wrinkles

Overeating

Excess of animal products, overeating, liver fatigue

Red ears – kidney trouble, circulatory disorders

Bags under the eyes – kidney fatigue, excess of water

A second bag – intestinal disorders

Red nose – heart trouble

Cheeks that are too red – weak lungs

Vertical groove – sexual force, vitality, longevity

A groove on the septum between the two nostrils – heart weakness

Swollen top lip – stomach disorder

Swollen bottom lip – intestinal disorders

Swollen chin – kidney troubles

Groove in chin – sexual vigour, vitality

Figure 40. Diagnostic signs of the face.

The Eyes

The eyes are the mirrors of physical health and the windows of the soul. Many traditional sayings allude to this relationship between the eye and our physical and mental health. Just as everywhere else in the body, all the parts of the body are represented in the eye but, as befits the organ of vision, more clearly and fully there than anywhere else.

An examination of the iris can provide a complete and minute diagnosis of our whole body. It shows the present state of health, past diseases and old physical and mental disorders. Everything is recorded there. In the accompanying sketch we have illustrated the different parts of the body as located in the iris of the left eye. The sketch has been

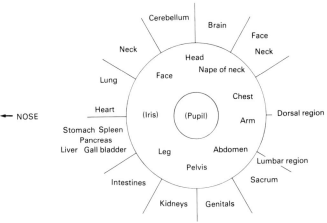

Figure 41. Simplified diagram of the iris and of the white of the left eye.

1 – Push upward. Strengthens the leg on the same side.
2 – Push downward. Strengthens the arm.

Figure 42. Connections between the eyes and the limbs.

deliberately simplified. Those who are interested in iris diagnosis should refer to the specialized books on the subject, while making sure to test every statement made in these books, because iris diagnosis, although basically simple, is also complex and the authors do not always agree on details. However, it is quite easy to confirm that the whole body is reflected in the iris from the head to the anus and including the limbs.

The fibres and colour of the iris with their flaws, such as spots, pits, clouds, etc. allow a diagnosis to be made. The zones present in the iris extend into the white of the eye and the functional anomalies of the organs reveal themselves there as tints and marks in the white surface: yellow (liver), greenish (cancer), brown spots (calculi) and milky white (mucus).

The eyes have a close connection with the liver and when the liver is functioning badly the eyes ache. When a person has eaten too much or had a meal that is Yin (sweets, alcohol) the eyes are tired and have circles round them and do not bear the light very well. The eyes of a person in good health bear everything: blinding light, cold and wind without crying, onions etc. The brilliancy of the eyes depends on what is eaten. A person in good health does not need sunglasses. Our eyes betray our thoughts, good or bad, our kindness and our unkindness etc. Frequent blinking (more than three times a minute) is a sign of organic weakness.

In women the eyes are linked with the ovaries and in men with the testicles. Sexual excess is revealed by black circles around the eyes. In men, the eyes should be small and almond-shaped. In women, they should be bigger and rounder (Yin). If the kidneys are overworked by too much drink, especially alcohol, the eyes become tired and sensitive and the puffy lower eyelids form 'bags' under the eyes. A further pouch can form under the first; it hangs down beside the nose and indicates a degeneration of the intestines. It is often seen in the elderly.

This short summary is simply intended to show the importance of the eyes. Numerous nerves converge there. These are very complete and very sensitive, so when performing Do-in care should be taken to treat the eyes very gently.

1. The first step is to charge the fingers thoroughly by rubbing the hands.

2. Place the tips of the 3 largest fingers between the superciliary arch and the eyeball and press gently in time with the heart beats some twenty times, while pushing upwards and while gradually increasing the pressure (Figure 43).

3. Repeat the process underneath the eyeball where the bony rim can be felt, and press downwards (Figure 44).

4. Using your two thumbs, press simultaneously on the outer corners of the eyes from the temples and

Figure 43.

Figure 44.

draw the thumbs towards the insides of the eyes. In this way you will first squeeze the bony borders of the eyes and then the borders of the eyeball itself (liver) (Figure 45).

5. Continue the action by placing the pads of the thumbs on the eyeballs and by maintaining the pressure for a certain time (Figure 46).

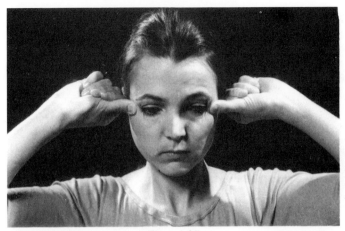

Figure 45.

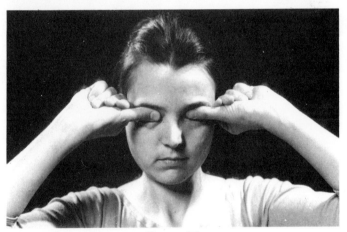

Figure 46.

6. Following this, rub your hands vigorously to warm them as much as possible and place the 'heels' of the hands on the eyeballs in such a way as to efficiently close the bony cavity of the eye. Press lightly to warm the eyes and meditate for an instant. This also warms the eyes and recharges them with energy — with magnetism, prana, ki; the effect being

Figure 47.

Figure 48.

to rest all the little muscles, to dilate the vessels and to stimulate the circulation (Figure 47),

7. Then slightly withdraw your hands from the bony cavity to form two cup-shapes. The palms will now no longer be pressing on the eyelids and the eyes should be turned in all directions — up and down, from side to side and in clockwise and anticlockwise

circles. This exercise is excellent for stimulating the liver (Figure 48).

8. Finally, stretch the eyelids very gently by loosening them from the surface of the eyes, then shut the eyes very tight at least three times.

The Nose

The nose is related to the circulatory system, the heart, the genitals, the digestive system and the lungs. The larger the nose, the more powerful is the digestive tract. It is good for a man to have a strong nose: a tiny nose in a man denotes weak sexuality and impulsiveness or lack of resolve.

The nostrils correspond to the lungs and they ought to be large and well open. A permanently red, swollen nose (sometimes even purple-coloured and with visible venules) indicates dilation of the heart and serious disturbances in the circulation of the blood. An excess of liquid, especially of alcohol, raises the blood pressure and the nose reddens. If the circulatory system is weak, this happens much more easily.

When the weather is very cold or very hot, our bodies have to adjust to the extreme temperature and this can involve circulatory troubles and the nose turns red or purple according to our state of health (usually the ears react similarly).

1. Pinch the root of the nose between the two eyes (this increases the mental concentration).

2. Rub the base of the nose on both sides with the index fingers from top to bottom along the cheek bones and cheeks (aids the digestion in the stomach and the large intestine). (See Figure 49).

The Cheek Bones

The cheek bones are mainly related to the lungs.

1. Stretch the skin over the cheek bones from the nose towards the ears by using the flat of the three largest fingers.

2. Exert pressure with the tip of the middle finger and make small circular movements near the bone of the nose (this clears the sinuses).

3. Massage under the cheek bones with the thumbs, looking for any sore spots, and restore the circulation of energy.

4. Massage the sides of the nose with the tips of the index fingers and continue with firm circular massage to the bottom of the sides of the nose.

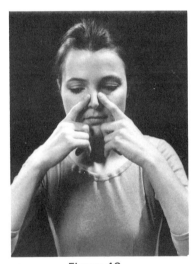

Figure 49.

The Cheeks

The cheeks are related to the intestines, and puffy cheeks are a sign of intestinal disorders. In the elderly, the tissues of the cheeks actually break down in extreme cases and this indicates a degeneration of the intestines.

1. Charge the hands by rubbing one against the other and chafe the cheeks from below, moving upwards (this stimulates digestion).

2. Pat the cheeks with the flats of the fingers quite vigorously.

Figure 50.

3. Effective massage can be performed on both lips simultaneously by applying the edge of the hand, between the thumb and the index finger, on the top lip at the roots of the teeth, and the other on the bottom lip and then 'sawing' them inversely while pressing as hard as you wish (Figure 50).

4. Massage the top lip and gum (at the roots of the teeth) working across the lip with some pressure.

5. There is a point in the centre of the gum under the nose, which you can massage in the morning to make yourself fully awake. It can also be treated in the event of fainting or heart trouble; in this case, the finger should be placed underneath the lip and the gum should be massaged directly.

6. Massage the bottom lip and gum in the same way.

The Mouth

The mouth reflects the entire condition of the digestive tract. The top lip is related to the stomach; the right and left corners of the mouth represent the duodenum and the bottom lip represents the intestines. A swollen upper lip indicates stomach troubles. In some people it is easy to observe that the top lip is swollen after a meal. Small pimples at the corners of the lips generally indicate irritation of the duodenum and disorders of the liver and gall bladder.

A swollen bottom lip corresponds to distension of the intestines. In this state the lip can be swollen, hard and red, in which case the intestines are congested; or swollen and soft with the mouth open, in which case the intestines are dilated and relaxed. Pale lips are a sign of anaemia of the digestive tube, whereas a red to purple colour shows congestion. The lips ought to be a pale pink.

The inside of the mouth is also an indicator of our state of health, and we need hardly remark that the tongue should be pink and clean. A very red tongue indicates congestion of the digestive system. The tongue also reveals the state of the uterus in women. A long upper lip, that is to say a big space between the nose and the mouth, is a good sign of vitality and sexual power. But, when the two vertical lines are missing, it is a sign that vitality is low and sexual power is weak. In man this lip should be high and the moustache should grow vigorously. Little vertical wrinkles all round the mouth are signs of sexual degeneration in women (usually after the menopause).

A horizontal wrinkle between the nose and the mouth is a bad sign in a woman and indicates frigidity, harshness, and intolerance of men – all bad omens for married life.

Note
The best Do-in of the day is done during meals, i.e. chewing food. All the facial muscles are exercised and the centres linked with the various organs are massaged and stimulated (the appetite is encouraged by the very act of eating). After thorough mastication, the stomach begins to secrete digestive juices in preparation for receiving the bolus of food from the mouth. Also, the palate is the crossroads where the terrestrial energies rising through the body to the tongue meet the celestial energies descending through the head to the uvula. The energies fuse together in the palate and mix with the food, which is thus charged and spiritualized more and more the longer it stays in contact with the palate and the more the meal is eaten in an atmosphere of calm and composure.

So the body owes a large part of its energy to this mastication. You will surely have noticed that it is very refreshing to slowly chew a nice piece of bread, even though there has not been time for the nutrients of the bread to be digested and assimilated. In addition, the pressure exerted on the teeth and gums by chewing guarantees good circulation and prevents tooth decay.

The Chin

The chin is related to the kidneys, the urinary passages and the genitals, and ought to be firm. A cleft chin is a good sign of vitality and sexual prowess. On the other hand, a puffy chin signals degeneration of the renal, urinary and sexual functions.

1. Press, squeeze and pat the chin with the fingertips.

2. Massage underneath the lower jaw with the tips of the thumbs. This stimulates the lymphatic circulation.

3. Work the thumbs upwards until they are under the ears, taking special care to massage in the cavity under the ear lobe to improve the functioning of the inner ear and to aid in the elimination of the mucus that accumulates there.

The Ears

The ear is an image of the development of the human being as an embryo. If development proceeds well, with plenty of nourishment from the mother and a life without stress, the foetus will have well-formed ears. It is possible to diagnose the state of health of a new-born baby and to assess its vitality from its ears. As may be seen in Figure 51, the ear is related to the whole body and there is a perfect correlation between it and the body of a baby in the foetal position with its head down.

Some acupuncturists confine treatment to the ears, where they find energy points related to all parts of the body. In every civilization, both ancient and modern, the ear has occupied a special place recognized by various customs.

Women have used ornate ear-rings to make themselves more attractive and men and children have sometimes worn little gold rings in one or both ears (according to their nationality) to prevent eye infections, to attract energy, vitalize the body and increase sharpness of vision.

The ear supplies information about the predispositions of the individual. The lower part is related to the vegetative, physical and material aspects of life and, when well developed, is a sign of vitality. The middle part of the ear reflects our involvement in intellectual life; in ears that are big and round there is a predisposition to intellectual activity. The upper part of the ear when well formed reveals spiritual aspirations. These things are inherited by us at birth; afterwards much depends on our circumstances and on what spiritual, mental and physical nourishment we receive.

The life in each part of the ear is related to the things we eat. Its upper part depends chiefly on proteins, its middle part on carbohydrates and its lower part on minerals. Here is yet another demonstration of the need for a well-balanced diet. A close look at the ear can therefore provide us with useful information about our state of health and about our dietary balance. For instance, if the lobe grows thin and hollow or puckers, the vitality is low and if the whole of the external ear is red there is a general disturbance of the kidneys and circulatory system.

It is amusing to think that we learnt our first Do-in lesson at school when the teacher pulled our ear to make us pay attention!

1. Set to work on the two ears simultaneously.

2. Stretch the lobe (this stimulates the keenness of the sight mainly).

3. Pull the middle part towards the back (this reinforces the energy of the arms).

4. Pull the upper part of the ear flap in an upward direction (this energizes the legs).

5. Carefully squeeze and massage the whole circumference of the ear.

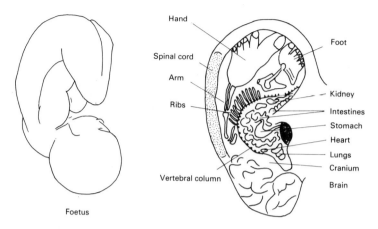

Figure 51. Correspondences of the ear.

6. Massage the inside of the external ear (the auricle), following the outlines of the grooves (sulci) with the tip of the index finger, and finish by inserting the finger into the ear and vibrating it. One should be careful not to poke too hard or too deeply, however.

7. Rub the hands together vigorously to warm them well and pass them backwards and forwards over the ears several times, pulling the ear flaps with them.

8. Move the index finger up behind the ears from bottom to top and then fold the ears forwards and down, rather like a cat washing its ears with its paws. This helps to regulate the body's temperature.

9. Place one cupped hand over one of your ears and rap the back of this hand in time with the heart-beat with the tips of the fingers of the other hand (this stimulates the activity of the kidneys). (Figure 52).

10. With the thumbs, massage all the cavities under and behind the ears in order to disperse stagnant energy. The effect of this is to stimulate the activity of the inner ear.

Figure 52.

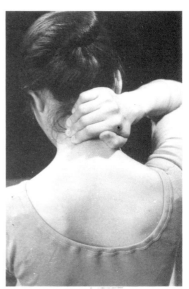

Figure 53.

The Neck

1. After feeling all around the external ear, continue beneath the base of the skull on each side of the spinal column and in the axis above the first cervical vertebra.

2. Massage the nape of the neck while holding it with the whole hand, the fingers on one side of the spine

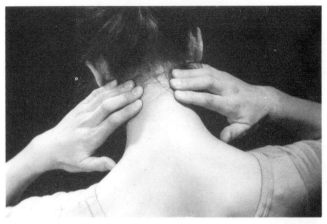

Figure 54.

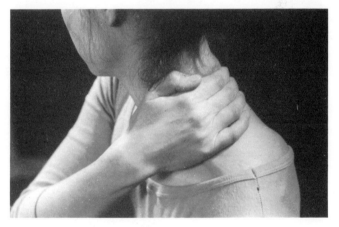

Figure 55.

and the heel of the hand on the other, and descend to the base of the neck. Change hands and repeat several times until the neck feels nice and warm (Figure 53).

3. Use the fingertips to massage each side of the cervical vertebrae, pulling them away from the spine and in a downward direction while keeping them in contact with the skin (Figure 54).

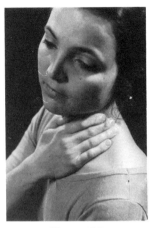

Figure 56.

4. Lay the flat hand as far back as possible at the base of the neck, pressing well. Then draw the hand round to the front so that it travels along the base of the neck. At the same time turn the head against the motion. Finish by bringing the fingers right to the front and into the hollow above the breast-bone between the two collar-bone ends. Slip the fingers into this hollow until they rest on the bony top of the sternum.

5. Repeat this massage at least three times on each side of the neck (Figures 55 to 57).

This massage of the base of the neck is excellent for relieving, steadying and toning up the heart. The final massage in the hollow above the sternum treats the lungs and the throat (asthma, cough).

Massaging the cervical vertebrae and neck eliminates contractures, restores the free movement of the vertebrae and improves the circulation of the blood in the cervical part of the spinal column and in the brain. There are many good effects, especially for headaches, stiff neck, insomnia, troubles with the eyesight and bloodshot eyes (the nape of the neck is also related to the body as a whole through the cervical vertebrae). Thick, dark blood, which would be better eliminated by cupping, often accumulates in the base of the neck at the top of the shoulders. The spots where the cupping glasses should be placed are indicated in Figure 63a. This practice is excellent for detoxication and stimulating circulation to the neck generally. Before placing the glass, prick the skin at three points and when the glass is in place, massage on each side to induce the flow of blood.

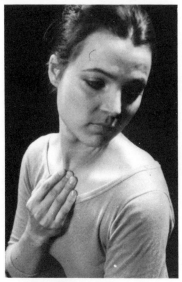

Figure 57.

The Throat

1. Turn your head slightly to make the muscle joining the ear to the top of the breast-bone stand out. Using the pad of the thumb, gently trace the inner part of the muscle in a downward direction. Repeat several times on each side. This stimulates the thyroid, the parathyroids and the local circulation of blood. (Figure 58).

2. Stroke and gently massage the trachea from top to bottom.

3. Tap gently with the flats of the fingers on each side of and on the front of the trachea (the same effects).

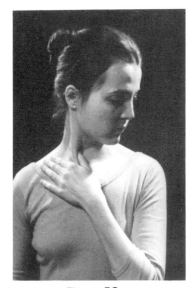

Figure 58.

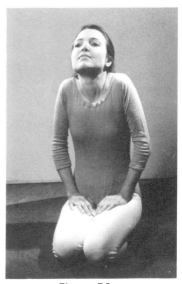

Figure 59.

4. Massage below the chin with the fingers of both
hands and work back down the outside of the throat
(sexual organs, aphrodisiac zone).

Limbering Up the Neck

The neck reflects our age. When we are young it is firm and
supple, but when we are old it is either withered and stiff or
fat (without muscle) and stiff.

Figure 60.

The nape of the neck becomes set during the course of the day, owing to fatigue and tension, and may even grow painful. The shoulders are raised, the eyebrows are knitted and it takes more and more energy to concentrate. There is no point in lowering the shoulders by an act of will because the shoulders rise and the neck seizes up again as soon as our attention wanders. Life involves a process of becoming tense then relaxing (Yang-Yin etc). When tensions appear, far from fighting them, act in the same direction and push them to the limit; then relaxation will come of its own accord.

1. Take a deep breath, raise the shoulders as high as you can and throw them back a little, push your head down between the shoulders and contract the neck as much as possible. Press your shoulders against the back of your head and retain this position for a moment while keeping your lungs full, then relax suddenly while breathing out (Figure 59).

2. Repeat three times at least.

3. Do the same thing while compressing the front of the neck (the throat and the thyroid gland). In addition to the relaxation that follows the compression, this practice produces an intense

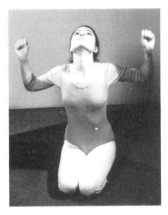

Figure 61.

irrigation and recharges the whole of the neck with prana, the effect being to fill you full of energy (Figure 60).

4. After the neck feels warm and relaxed, cross your arms behind your back, hold yourself very straight, with your head in line with your back and carry out the following head movements, breathing out each time at the end of a movement:
   (i)   from front to back;
   (ii) from right to left;
   (iii) to one side by lowering the ear towards the shoulder;
   (iv) rotation of the head on the neck in both directions.

5. Perform these exercises as often as you like, but at least twenty times.

6. Then shake your head in all directions as much as you like.

7. Finally, clench your fists with your thumbs inside your fingers, raise your arms at an angle of 45° to the vertical as you take a very deep breath and, while keeping your lungs full, pull your shoulders back and bend your head back so as to squeeze the

nape of your neck against your shoulders as much as possible. Clench your fists even tighter for a moment and then suddenly let go while breathing out and let your arms drop (Figure 61).

8. Repeat this three times.

THE CHEST AND SHOULDERS

The shoulders, too, are related to the whole body. A helpful way of remembering the correspondence is to imagine the body of a man laid out on the shoulder with his head at the base of the neck and his pelvis and legs at the extremity of the shoulder (Figure 62). Figure 3, illustrating the meridians, also shows the importance of the shoulders by the way the meridians pass through them, especially those of the intestines. Stiffness in the shoulders often indicates troubles in the intestines, the liver (right-sided pain) and of the stomach (left-sided pain).

The shoulders, together with the nape of the neck, are where emotional tensions accumulate. The human body should be firm and strong below, in the legs and abdomen. This is the pedestal or root (Yang). It should be supple and flexible (Yin) above, with the shoulders and neck supporting the head like a stalk supporting its flower.

1. In order to stretch and limber up the shoulders, after exercising the neck, interlock your arms as shown in Figures 63b and 64. Thus, place the left elbow in the inside fold of the right arm so that it pokes out to the right of the right arm; and place the right hand on the left hand, palm to palm and thumb to thumb and bring the two hands to the level of the face. The right hand is invariably a little lower than the left hand. Now breathe in deeply while keeping the arms firmly interlocked and, as you breathe in,

your body will stretch between the shoulder blades. Breathe out while extending the arms without releasing the contact between your hands and keeping the left elbow well tucked into the right arm without allowing it to escape to the left (Figure 65).

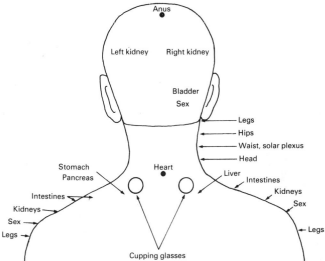

Figure 62. Correspondences of the shoulders.

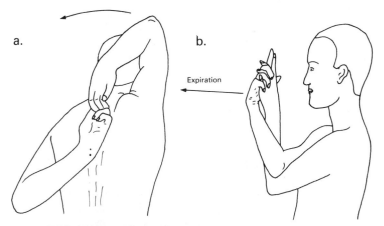

Figure 63.   Limbering up the shoulders.
    63a. Limbering up the 'awkward zone' between the shoulder blades.
    63b. Stretching the trapezius muscles.

Figure 64.

Figure 65.

2. Do the same thing on the right side, with the arms
   the other way round. Repeat at least three times.
   This is an excellent exercise for stretching the
   shoulder and the trapezius muscles in particular.

3. Next, using both hands, give a strong massage to
   the shoulders, the base of the neck, the trapezius
   muscles and the deltoids. Knead the trapezius and

deltoid muscles well and then squeeze the trapezius muscles and pull them forward.

4. Strike the shoulders, the deltoids, the front of the shoulders on the clavicles with your cupped hand and then with the half-closed fist held very loosely.

We now come to a very important exercise designed to unblock the shoulder joints, the top of the dorsal section of the backbone and the part situated between the shoulder blades. The latter area has been called the 'awkward zone', because it is difficult to reach and treat. Nevertheless, it is most important (see Figure 3 showing the meridians there and the way the vertebrae correspond to various physiological functions and to particular organs). The zone is not usually very active and it is the first one to grow old and hard. It is always there that a person begins to hunch up and to get blockages – the zone loses its vitality and degenerates and so do the corresponding functions.

1. Hold your hands behind your back as in Figure 63a, with one arm bent behind the back, elbow down, and the other arm bent behind the head, elbow up. If at first you are unable to clasp the hands, dangle a piece of string from the uppermost hand and seize this with the lower one. Little by little, as you pull on

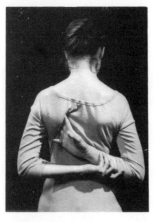

Figure 66.

the string, you will shorten the gap until you can grip fingers.

2. Stand up nice and straight and tug with the upper arm as high as possible and as far back as possible against the head. Then take a deep breath and expand your chest as much as you can while trying to arch the back. (This is excellent for the heart. To vitalize the heart, it is necessary to give it room. This is the essential feature of all exercises designed to treat the heart.)

3. While in this position with the back very straight, lean to the right and to the left. You will hear the vertebrae at the top of the back being released and will feel the warmth and the flow of energy. The exercise may be completed by rotating the body.

4. Repeat with the arms exchanging positions.

Loosening of the Shoulder Blades

Following the preceding exercise, place one hand behind your back and feel for the opposite shoulder blade, helping yourself if necessary by pulling on your arm with your other hand, and poke your fingers as far as possible underneath the shoulder blade along as much of its length as can be managed. (This area relates to the stomach. Figure 66.)

The Chest

The correspondences of the front of the chest are as follows: (i) Above the breasts: The rib-cage and sternum — the lungs and pulmonary disorders. (ii) Below the breasts: The sternum — the heart and cardiac troubles; The ribs — the gall bladder and stomach.

1. Order of Do-in manipulations: Above the breasts, the sides, and along the sternum moving upwards, preferably with the lungs full.

2. Tapping with the flexible, half-closed fist.

3. Drumming with the slightly separated tips of the fingers.

4. Rubbing of the ribs at the top of the chest and vertically on the sides.

5. Place the flat of the hand on the breasts and pass it over the breasts while tapping on the tips of the fingers with the fist of the other hand; then place the fingers of the hand held flat on the intercostal spaces on each side and tap with the fist several times. Move up along the sternum with the fingers flat and touching each other, while tapping on their tips to make the thorax resonate.

6. Massage the points of the lungs under the collar bone with the thumbs (Figure 2).

Once the top of the body — the arms, shoulders, head, neck and chest — have been thoroughly revived and revitalized, the energy in that area can circulate freely. One can take advantage of this satisfactory state by doing some breathing exercises and taking in big draughts of prana. One should stand to do this.

If you have remained in the Seisa position during the first stage of Do-in, your knees and ankles can be painful — so do not get up too suddenly.

1. While still seated, extend your legs in front of you without stretching them completely.

2. Put the palms of your hands on your knees and give the kneecaps circular massage. The simple contact of the hands stimulates the circulation and warms the whole body.

3. At the same time, stretch the feet: as one foot is pointed forward and the instep is stretched, the toes of the other foot are drawn towards the body and the Achilles tendon is stretched (Figure 67).

4. Continue in this way without stopping, gradually stretching your legs until they are resting on the floor, extended, relaxed and free of any pain.

5. When this point is reached, rotate the feet.

Rotation towards the inside contracts the bones and joints of the ankle and foot and drives out the water. Rotation towards the outside, on the other hand, relaxes the joints and the energy circulates more freely.

1. Perform the rotations in the two directions.

2. Next strike the backs of the legs on the floor after raising the knees a little. This vibration and massage will do you a great deal of good. Treat the backs of the legs in this way as strongly as you feel the need.

3. Then, while expelling as much air as you can from the lungs, contract the legs as much as possible and square the feet, i.e. draw the toes towards you and stretch the Achilles tendon. Concentrate on making a contraction at the knees and ankles, then gradually relax the contraction while breathing in. The result is complete relaxation of the legs.

4. You can then stand up to carry out your breathing exercises.

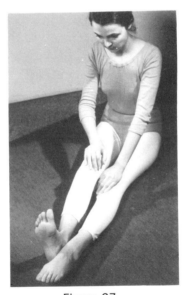

Figure 67.

Respiration – the Intake of Prana
Total Expiration (the Yang phase)
The first phase consists of emptying the lungs totally – something we fail to do in everyday life.

1. Stand up with your feet spread the same distance apart as your shoulders. With your legs slightly bent and your body leaning forward, your hands on your knees, breathe out as thoroughly as possible. At the end of this outward breath, open the rib cage as if you were going to inhale, but do not breathe in air. Hold this position for a few seconds and then expire once more while closing the rib cage again. You will be surprised to find that on the second occasion you will expel almost as much air as you did originally.

2. Repeat the expansion of the rib cage several times and, little by little, reject all the residual air of the lungs. At the end of this total emptying *take care* – do *not* breathe in suddenly but allow the abdomen to rise again, relax and only then draw breath.

If the intake of air is too rapid it will expand the alveoli (the tiny air-sacks within the lungs) rather roughly and they may suffer injury. Should you make this mistake you will be aware of tiny pin-pricks of pain in the thorax and you must then wait several days before beginning again.

The practice just described involves the following mechanism. When you have expelled the air that leaves the lungs readily, the expansion of the rib cage puts the residual air in the poorly ventilated zones of the lungs in circulation. And so, you eventually remove all the air, even from those places where it is difficult to replace it.

Total Inspiration (the Yin phase)
Now you can set to work and refill your lungs to their maximum capacity. The fresh air will be able to penetrate all the zones and especially the upper part of the chest, where air-exchange is usually poor.

Breathe in fully while raising your arms, then lower your arms without exhaling, and renew the effort to breathe in while raising your arms again. You will discover that you can now inhale almost as much air as you did the first time, etc. Continue this pumping action of the arms, breathing in air as you raise them and retaining it as you lower them, until the chest is completely expanded. Then breathe out gently.

The process is the same as that mentioned under 'Total Expiration' only in reverse. First of all you admit air to the zones that usually receive it easily. Then, as you lower your arms, you relax your chest and bring your ribs into play and the air then reaches all zones. You can then breathe in as described. When performing this exercise you will feel the top of your chest expanding under the internal pressure and this is the zone where expansion is most needed.

Loosening the Pleura and Putting the Lungs to Work

While standing or, preferably, sitting in the Seisa pose, open the rib cage as much as possible. Inhale without allowing the cage to move or close. Work solely with your diaphragm and abdominal muscles.

Many people when they inhale and exhale hardly use their diaphragm at all, and their lungs simply follow the movements of the rib cage without moving freely inside the cage. Consequently some parts suffer from adhesions and the circulation of blood and oxygen is impaired in these places due to the loss of movement and of suppleness in the tissues. The affected zones become foci of infection, susceptible to pleurisy, bronchitis, etc.

Practising the proposed exercises will eventually break down the adhesions. At the start you will experience great difficulty in carrying out this form of respiration but, little by little, the lungs will move freely inside the rib cage. It should not be forgotten that it is the lungs which do the breathing, not the rib cage; you could have a huge rib cage, yet the inside of the lungs could be hard, sclerosed and unfit for respiration.

Persian Windmills

1. Stand really erect with your abdomen pulled in, your back straight, your chest high and your chin tucked in.

2. Stretch and raise the arms alternately and swing them round from the front to the back.

3. Take special care not to bend the arms but keep them vertical to the shoulders without lateral displacement, and pull well on the rib cage. If it will help, you can hold a small weight in each hand, such as a dumb-bell or piece of stone. To begin with, breathe in when raising the arm and breathe out when lowering it. Afterwards, when the rhythm has been established, breathe in during several rotations and breathe out during several rotations.

If you have the time, you can repeat the exercise while reversing the direction in which you swing your arms, i.e. from back to front. Then you can also repeat the breathing exercises with the two arms together.

These exercises may also be performed when seated or even when lying down. They bring about a considerable increase in the capacity of the lungs (and do not forget that the cerebral capacity is a function of the power of respiration).

Turning to the Sun (Persian yoga)
Once you have perfected the previous exercise, you can then perform a complete pranic exercise. There are many of these but the one we should like to suggest is one of the exercises of Persian yoga, a corrective type of yoga suitable for Western man.

1. Stand up straight without stiffness. If the legs are stiff this will affect the whole posture and, in particular, produce tension in the abdominal viscera. Put your weight on the soles of the feet and not on your heels and sway backwards and forwards a little to find your balance.

2. Breathe as described in the previous exercise while turning your arm right round the shoulder. Keep breathing in during a certain number of swings. Breathe out during the same number of rotations while swinging from back to front. At the end of

your exhalation make yet another half-rotation to bring the arm to the vertical; stretch it upwards as high as possible, tight to the head and with your fist firmly closed. During the time the arm is being raised, make a full and rapid inhalation. Then, bend the trunk rapidly forward and hit the ground with your fist while retaining your breath. Exhale gently as you rise so that your arm once more points upward, and then let your arm drop back and swing backwards and forwards like a pendulum until it comes to a stop. Do the same with the other arm.

3. Do not force yourself but gradually increase the number of respiratory rotations. Do not exceed more than seven rotations to each inhalation and seven to each exhalation. Take the trouble to carry out the exercise as perfectly as possible, with freedom of movement, thoroughly relaxed but with concentration.

When doing this exercise, turn to face the east at sunrise, the south at noon and the west at sunset and the north at night. The position of your body, the gyratory movement, the mode of respiration and the vibratory shock-wave transmitted to your body, set up a harmony with the electromagnetic vibrations and solar and terrestrial radiations. You will immediately feel stimulated by this practice.

THE WAIST

After the breathing exercises, continue with exercises designed to improve your figure.

If you already do yoga (hatha yoga), you can use for this purpose the series of triangles. We suggest you try one of them.

1. With your legs apart, raise your arm above your head, holding it pressed against your ear, and take a deep breath. Turn the opposite foot outwards in line with your shoulders (Figure 68) and bend sideways as shown while holding the breath. Breathe out as you rise. Pay attention to keeping the weight of the body evenly distributed on your two feet as you bend over. This entails using the whole pelvis.

This exercise has different effects from those where the hands are clasped behind the back. In the latter, the shoulders and the top of the back are lowered as a single unit without doing much work: it is mainly the waist that is stretched. What happens is a stretching of the structure of the body and of the meridians and a deep massage of all the organs situated in the region of the waist: the liver, gall bladder, spleen, pancreas, stomach and kidneys.

2. Another way of doing this stretching is as follows: put your feet together, raise both arms with their hands joined and bend over to right and left while exhaling.

Figure 68. Exercise for improving the figure.

This exercise has the same effects as the preceding one. In particular, it helps the stomach to open towards the duodenum (at the pyloric end), and this, when aided by massage, gets rid of those residual substances in the stomach which, if they remain there too long, cause acidity.

3. You may also carry out rotations of the trunk of the body with your legs apart, by flinging your arms to the right and to the left but without forcing them backwards too much.

Limbering up the lower part of the body

1. Put your feet together from heel to toe along their whole length, and keeping them flat on the ground without lifting your heels place your hands on your knees and crouch down as much as possible (this is fine for tensing the kidneys and the Achilles tendon). With practice you will soon be able to sit on the backs of your ankles. Inhale as you lower your body and remain in position for a moment while you hold your breath. Get up again by pressing on your knees with your hands and tensing your legs. Exhale at the same time.

2. Repeat three times at least.

3. Keeping your feet together and your hands on your knees, describe circles with your knees, first in one direction and then in the other, as you lower your body more and more.

4. Keep your hands on your knees and place your feet as wide apart as possible. Then, without moving your feet, swing your body over each one of them in turn by turning it right and left. Always try to keep your buttocks as close to the ground as possible when you swing your body from side to side. This exercise is especially good for the crotch and all its associated functions.

5. Sit down and perform Do-in on your feet.

THE LEGS AND FEET

Our feet support the body — they are its pedestal, so to speak. Trouble at this level has repercussions on the whole body. We should support ourselves naturally on the soles of our feet with our weight evenly distributed. The body is like a vibrating string (Yin-Yang) and any distortion at the level of the heels has its effects at the head.

As above, so below.* A faulty position of the feet creates problems in the nape of the neck. It often happens that the neck is unsuccessfully treated for pain. The answer is to treat the feet or to change one's shoes. The custom of wearing high heels produces the bad posture illustrated in Figure 69, where the bends in the spinal column are accentuated:

> The nape of the neck is too curved, causing a bad position of the head and a bad position of the eyes in their sockets, with the eye-muscles working abnormally (tension) to keep the line of sight directly ahead.

> An abnormal position of the cervical vertebrae and thus abnormal functioning of certain organs.

> Stagnation of dark blood in the nape of the neck, poor irrigation, poisoning and functional disturbance, especially those affecting the sight (myopia).

> A round back and blockages in the 'awkward zone'.

> Curvature in the lumbar zone of the back with a predisposition to lumbago and sciatica, impaired

*A well-known hermetic axiom. *Translator's note.*

functioning of the kidneys and of the urinary passages, the genitals and intestines.

A paunch with poor suspension of the abdominal organs and prolapse tendencies.

Loss of the hara which is too high and too forward, as found in nearly all Westerners; hence the basic instability of their bodies which tend to fall forwards. To avoid this, there is a compensatory contraction in the back. The individual, however, is not at ease, he is off-centre, unstable, tense and anxious.

The knees project slightly, and this is an abnormal position.

Later, we will look at the relations between posture and the stomach, liver and eyes.

A glance at the soles of the shoes will tell us a lot about the position of the feet and about the whole posture of the body. If there is too much wear at the heels, the person is Yin; if there is too much wear in front, he is Yang. If the outer edge is rather worn, the person is Yin, but if the instep is more worn he is Yang. When normal, the wear should be even, with a slight emphasis under the big toe and thus a little more in front on the inside (Yang). For preference, the weight should bear on the inner edge of the foot. This part is related to the heart and emotions etc. For example, if you are surprised, your pulse begins to race and at the same time your legs flex and your knees come together to throw your

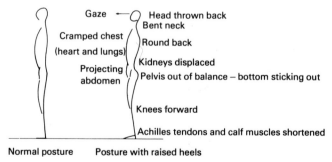

Figure 69. Normal and bad posture.

DO-IN

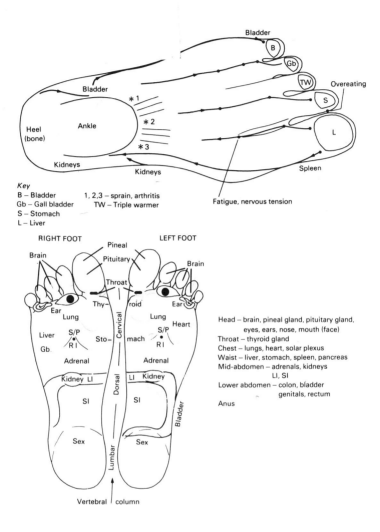

Figure 70. Correspondences of the points in the feet.

weight on your insteps. The emotion then ceases, the pulse slows down again and a state of calmness returns.

In the same way if, when seated on the floor with our legs stretched out, we swing our feet inwards, our heart will slow down and recover from any agitation. The very same will occur if we twist our feet inwards.

People's feet can tell us a great deal about their mental states. If the toes are curled in, the brain is tightened up too. Do the goose-step for three-quarters of a mile, stamping your heels on the ground, and you will soon discover the relationship between the feet and the brain. The same applies if you wear shoes with hard soles. We no longer walk on the soft ground but on concrete most of the time and at every step we take our body suffers a minor shock. The soles of our shoes should be capable of absorbing these shocks.

The foot is a very good example of how one part of the body is related to all other parts. We can find there connections with all the organs and with all our physical and mental functions. To verify this assertion, simply look at the pattern made by the soles of the feet when set side by side. The head can be thought of as occupying the level of the big toe and the pelvis can be assigned to the heels. It is easy to learn the geography of the energy centres on the soles of the feet (see Figure 70).

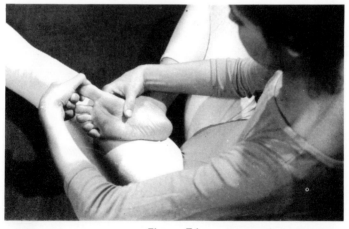

Figure 71.

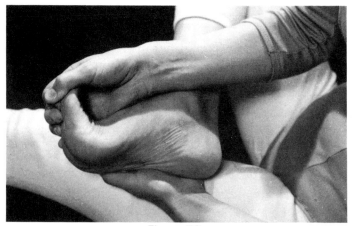

Figure 72.

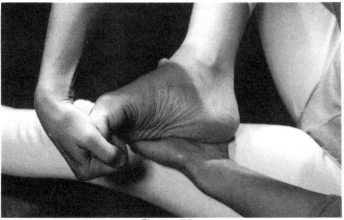

Figure 73.

Do-in of the feet is very like that of the hands.

1. Sit down, stretch out one leg and pull the other towards you until its foot is resting on the thigh of the straight leg.

2. Start with the toes, paying particular attention to the big toe as this is related to the liver, the pineal and pituitary glands, the head in general, to the sense of hearing and the throat.

3. Hold the big toe between your thumb and index finger on each side of the nail, squeeze it and rotate it in both directions as many times as possible, but at least twenty times (Figure 71).

4. Massage the top of the nail, the fleshy pad of the toe and the joints.

5. Pull the toe vigorously in a forward direction.

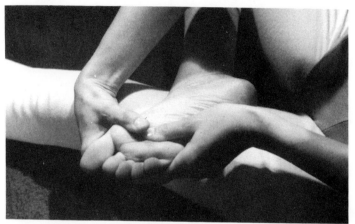

Figure 74.

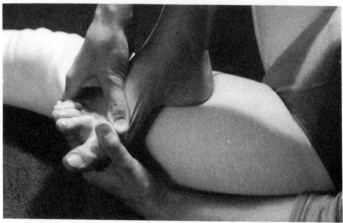

Figure 75.

Figure 76.

6. Turn it upwards and then curl it in towards the sole of the foot.

7. Do the same thing with each toe in turn (see the correspondences in Figure 70,) especially those beneath the toes — the points of the liver, the stomach and the gall bladder redden and become very sensitive if these organs are tired or functioning badly.

8. Massage and pinch the places between the toes.

9. Holding the toes in the palm, massage the crease at the base of the toes and bend the toes all together backwards and forwards (Figures 72 and 73).

10. Place your thumbs on the sole of the foot near the toes and twist the foot so that its sole is turned upwards (Figure 74); then, placing your thumbs on top of the foot, twist it round in the opposite direction (this calms the heart) (Figure 75).

11. Using the pads of both thumbs give deep massage to the entire sole of the foot.

12. Holding the heel in your palm, scratch the hollow arch of the foot in the direction of the heel with the

fingers of the same hand — this stimulates the sexual organs and treats kidney troubles (Figure 77).

13. Hold the back of the foot in the palm of your hand and turn the sole upwards, and then strike with your fist the entire sole and, in particular, the hollow of the arch (kidneys) (Figures 78 and 79).

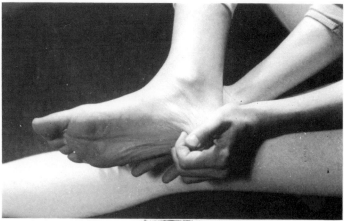

Figure 77.

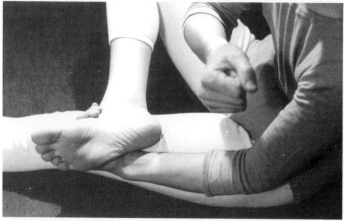

Figure 78.

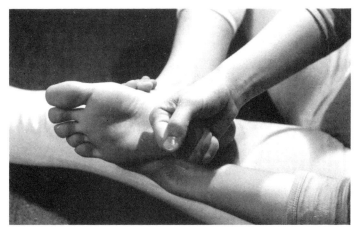

Figure 79.

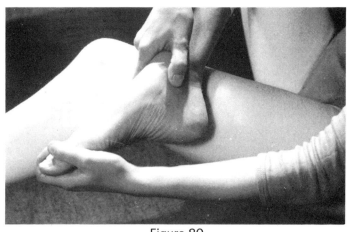

Figure 80.

14. In the same way, strike the inside edge of the foot, but more gently (vertebral column).

15. The same results are obtained by walking barefoot on pebbles or in the dew.

16. If you wish to treat your right foot, place your right elbow on your right knee and grip your ankle from above and at the top with your whole hand, so that

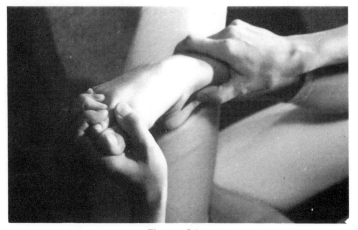

Figure 81.

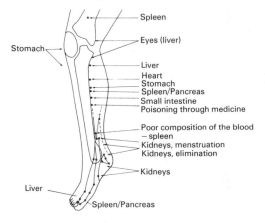

Fig. 82 Points of the ankle and leg.

your thumb is round the inside of the ankle and your fingers are round the outside of the ankle. Take your toes in your left hand and turn your foot several times in both directions, to make the ankle supple (Figures 80 and 81).

17. Keeping the right hand round the ankle, take the heel between the thumb and index finger of the left hand and lift and shake the foot (Figure 83).

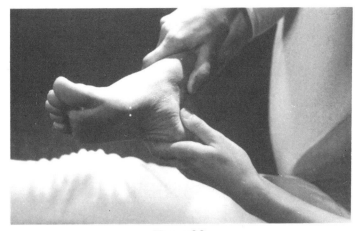

Figure 83.

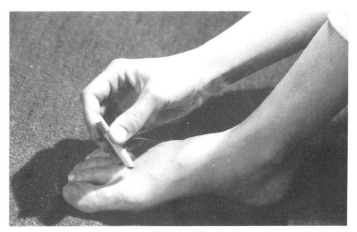

Figure 84.

18. Place the sole of the treated foot on the floor.

19. Using the fingers, massage the tops of the toes and the grooves between the metatarsals, working back towards the ankle. In between the big toe and the second toe, at the end of the groove that runs back from them along the top of the foot, there is a special sensitive point corresponding to

fatigue and nervous exhaustion. This should be massaged and heated with a cigarette held a little way away from it – either an ordinary cigarette or, better still, a mugwort cigarette (moxa). See Figure 84.

20. Massage the grooves with the pads of the thumbs and, at the same time, dig the nails of the fingers into the sole of the foot (Figure 85).

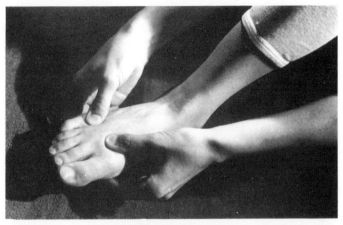

Figure 85.

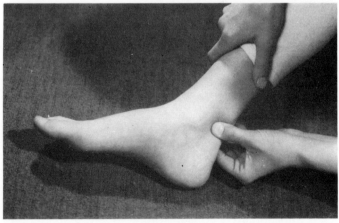

Figure 86.

21. Also make a point of treating, in the groove running back from between toes four and five, a vital reflex zone, i.e. the balance centre connected with the ears, the ears themselves being represented under the fourth and fifth toes.

These various types of massage on the top of the foot stimulate the circulation of energies in the meridians (liver, gall bladder and stomach).

22. Massage and knead the external edges of the foot (bladder), and then its internal edge (vertebral column); and, on the flat of the heel under the ankle, look for sore places in the bony hollows (kidneys, spleen).

23. Compress the foot crosswise with the hand to round it and to squeeze the metatarsals.

24. Massage the back of the heel with the thumb pads and hit the heel on the floor several times (this stimulates the regeneration of the bone cells and treats haemorrhoids, in the same way as tapping the top of the head).

The Ankle

1. Give the ankle a good rub with the palms of the hands to warm it up.

2. Look for any sore spots (as you did in the wrists) in all the hollows of the joints, and massage well the instep between the tendons (this is good for sprains and eliminates excess fluid).

The ankle is related, among other things, to the ears, as is the external malleolus and the bone going up to the calf. It is a good idea to warm this part up before hearing a concert. With supple feet one will have well-tuned ears and an open spirit. The ankle corresponds to the neck: the front, to the nape and the back to the throat. If the ankles are stiff, the neck is stiff and so is your character: a stiff neck brings with it errors of judgment. If your ankles and feet are cold and wet, you are in a bad mood, your ears become stopped up, your digestion gives you trouble and you are unable to sleep.

It is important to be attentive while performing Do-in on the feet and ankles, because a good diagnosis can be made by noting any sensitive points. The ankles are very eloquent; they should be lean with the skin tight against the bones. If the foot is swollen on the outside under the malleolus (sometimes becoming puffy with a pocket of water), malfunctioning of the bladder and the urinary passages is indicated. If, on the other hand, the inside of the ankle down to the hollow of the foot is swollen, sometimes with the appearance of blue veins, it is the kidneys that are affected.

The Achilles tendons are related to the kidneys, the urinary passages and the sexual organs. They too ought to be slender and it should not be possible to catch hold of the skin that covers them. Thick, fat skin corresponds to disorders of the above-mentioned functions.

They should be massaged and squeezed at the same time, while moving the thumb and fingers up in the direction of the calf. This treats sciatica, stimulates the kidneys, etc. (Figure 87).

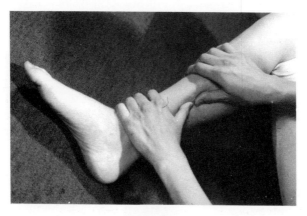

Figure 87.

The Legs
After pinching the Achilles tendon, proceed with Do-in of the leg itself.

1. Place your two thumbs tip to tip and massage with their pads the groove that lies all along the inside edge of the tibia from the ankle to the knee (Figure 87).

This groove between the bone and the tendon and the calf muscle, is rich in energy centres. Four important meridians pass through it: those of the kidneys, spleen-pancreas, liver and small intestines. In addition, there are connections through these meridians with other functions, chiefly those of the heart and stomach.

There are various methods of locating the points, but the simplest is to gently palpate the groove as you work your way up it and so discover the sensitive points. Should some point be very painful, do not bruise it, but for preference treat the same point on the other leg, which is often less sensitive.

2. Massage the grove in an upward direction at least three times. Then pass over the external surface of the leg, where there are two important meridians, that of the stomach and that of the gall bladder. Starting with the front edge of the tibia and going towards the back, there are long muscles from the base of the knee joint to the ankle.

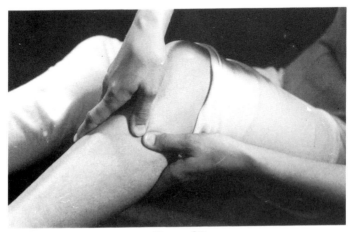

Figure 88.

3. Using your thumb pads, give this muscular part a deep massage. Start with the hollows found just under the knee joint and move down to the ankle (Figure 88).

At four fingers' breadths below the kneecap and at two fingers' widths behind the edge of the tibia, there is a very important point called 'san-ri'. This is a point on the stomach meridian but in fact when it is treated the whole body is

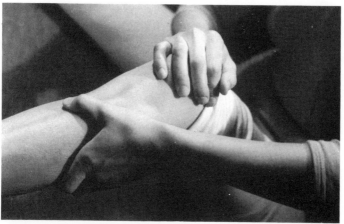

Figure 89.

Figure 90.

stimulated. When you are very tired, depressed or suffering from digestive disorders, you should treat this point every day, either by massage during Do-in or using heat in the way described earlier (p. 101).

4. Starting with this point, continue the massage down the stomach meridian as far as the ankle, making successive prods with the thumb pads.

Then place the flat of the hand on the outside of the leg with the thumb on the edge of the tibia, the palm on the part that has just been treated and the tips of the four fingers on the rear bony edge, where the gall bladder meridian runs. Massage by exerting pressure of the whole hand, the thumb, palm and fingers, and work downwards from the knee to the ankle several times (Figure 89).

5. Knead your calf with the whole hands, and work up from the Achilles tendon to the knee (intestines).

6. Using the two thumb pads, massage continuously in a downward direction, in the back axis of the leg, between the muscles of the calf, until you reach the top of the Achilles tendon (the bladder meridian). (See Figure 90). Press one of the important points in this meridian, in the hollow of the knee and massage gently (Figure 3).

The Knees

1. Without stopping the rubbing, move from the leg to the knee; warm it up as much as possible on each side and then on the top.

2. Next, massage all round the kneecap with the fingers and stretch the skin (elimination of water).

3. Press strongly on the top of the kneecap and make it move in every direction.

4. Massage all the bony parts to remove pains.

The knee is a very important chakra, related to the entire body. When the knees become stiff, this indicates poor elimination in the body as a whole. This is where deposits of toxins and waste products collect, such as those derived from medicines for example. To be more precise, the knees are related to the liver and stomach. If the sides of the kneecap are painful, especially the sides of the left kneecap, the position of the stomach is faulty, i.e. it is displaced downwards. Massage the painful part. The inside surface of the joint corresponds to the liver and to the eyes.

The Thighs

1. In this position, with the legs stretched out and relaxed, prolong the massage to the knee by kneading the calf muscles well with the whole hands.

2. Above the knee at the base of the femur on the inside surface there is a point that is easy to find when painful. It corresponds to menstrual problems in women and can be treated during the general massage of the thigh.

3. Men should squeeze the attachment of the internal muscles of the thigh, on the pubic bone, near the sexual organs (this strengthens sexual potency).

4. Then go on to perform Do-in on the other leg, including the calf, knee and thigh.

5. Next, with your legs extended and spread out a little and your knees slightly raised, strike your two legs simultaneously with the fleshy part of the hands, keeping the wrists flexible and the fists gently clenched. Begin with the internal malleolus of the ankle and then move up along the leg following the inside edge of the tibia to its border with the calf, the knee joint and the inside of the calves to the groin (Figure 91).

6. Then strike the legs on the outside from top to bottom, making sure that you keep your fists flat, lightly closed and your wrists supple. It is the backs of the bent fingers that make contact with the legs (Figure 92).

7. Work your way up the inside and down the outside at least three times.

8. With the back of the clenched fist, strike one of your legs with both hands, then the other, including the ankle, calf, knee and the under parts of the thighs, working on them thoroughly. Loosen your feet a little and then the calf and thigh muscles will be relaxed and will respond better to kneading.

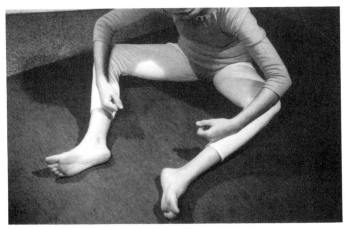

Figure 91.

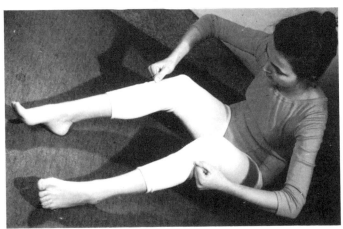

Figure 92.

9. Sit once more in the Seisa pose and resume the Do-in massage of your thighs on the three following surfaces: the outside surface (gall bladder), the top surface (stomach) and the inside surface (liver, spleen, pancreas, kidneys).

10. With the knuckle of your middle finger, rap the point you find to be most sensitive on the flat of

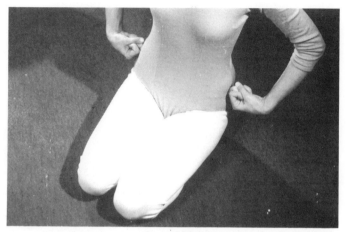

Figure 93.

your hip. This point is very important and you will be sure to find it; it corresponds to the gall bladder and to the genitals.

11. Repeat several times on both hips at the same time (Figure 93).

12. Then work downwards, all along the outside of the thigh, striking it with the flat of a loosely held wrist, with the backs of your clenched fists (Figure 94).

13. Clench your fists and, keeping the wrists supple, strike the tops of the thighs with the fleshy side of the hand, working your way down from where the thighs join the pelvis until you reach the knee. Repeat several times (Figure 95).

14. Spread your knees apart and repeat the same treatment several times, striking the insides of the thighs and working from the knees upward. (Figure 96).

Figure 94.

Figure 95.

Figure 96.

THE PELVIS

1. Strike all the bones at the back of the pelvis, sacrum and hips with loosely held wrists as often as you like.

2. Look for sore spots with your thumbs, in all the little bony hollows and in the hollows of the muscles at the back of the hips (sciatic nerves, urinary passages, genitals, anus).

3. Massage the upper edge of the pelvis all round the waist; dispersing and dissolving the sore spots (sluggish bowels, elimination of water). Pay special

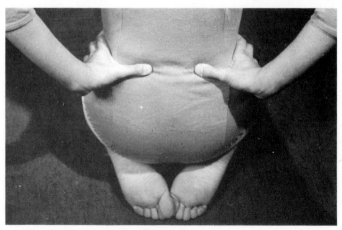

Figure 97.

attention near the attachment of the vertebral column (sciatic nerves), to decongest the base of the fifth lumbar vertebra, which rests like a socket on the sacrum and supports the whole weight of the body (Figure 97).

The Kidneys

The kidneys are most important, they represent the strength of the human being: the stronger the kidneys, the more robust their owner.

The kidneys are the centre of action, just as the stomach is the centre of vitality. Many people have great ideas and make splendid plans but achieve nothing because their kidneys are weak. It is the good health of our kidneys which rouses us to action and if we do nothing, although we are often unaware of the cause, the kidneys are to blame. When our kidneys are not functioning well we tend to be uneasy and timid and certainly not enterprising.

By the word 'kidneys' we mean the whole energy system behind the waist: the framework of the spinal column, the musculature and the organs. Hence, it is necessary to limber up the lumbar vertebrae, and to strengthen the muscles and organs (by exercises and a proper diet), to circulate the energy (by Do-in), and to avoid stress as anxiety upsets the kidneys.

Do-in for the kidneys:

1. Clench your fists and apply the knuckles of your index fingers to each side of the backbone on the long muscles that support it and rub vigorously to warm the kidney area well.

2. Strike the same part with your fists while keeping your wrists flexible, and reach up your back as high as possible.

3. Using the same knuckles, describe circles with them on each side of the vertebral column towards the vertebrae, moving up from the pelvis to the first floating ribs.

4. Do the same thing while digging in the thumbs and vibrating them.

5. Continue by massaging the ends of the second of the two pairs of floating ribs with your thumb pads. These are two very important points in the 'kidney system' and the kidneys can also be treated here using moxa (a herb used in a special method of warming points in the skin, described on p. 101) when pain is present (blockage of the kidneys, nephritic colic).

6. After this treatment, warm the kidney area once more by friction.

7. Sit cross-legged, bringing your knees up against your chest, and grip each of your crossed feet with the opposite hand (e.g. take the left foot in your right hand), and roll over on your back several times. This massages the spine and the bladder meridians (Figure 98).

8. After several rolls, stop and balance yourself on your buttocks at each return to a vertical position (Figure 99). Stopping successfully in this position requires intense concentration of energy in the hara, so this is a good way of strengthening it. Make sure you place your knees in the folds of your elbows.

9. Resume the Seisa pose and push back your feet to each side of your buttocks. Massage the soles of your feet and underneath your toes vigorously with your clenched fists, holding your arms straight so that you can use the whole weight of your body (Figure 100). This is an excellent foot massage which is very effective.

10. In this position, hammer your heels with your fists (this strengthens the bones).

Figure 98.

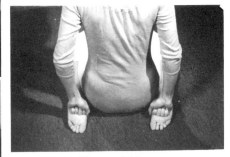

Figure 100.

Figure 99.

The Coccyx

The coccyx is related to the brain. Persistent headaches can be due to a dislocated coccyx.

1. Sitting as before with your feet on either side of your buttocks, place your fists on the underside of your toes and bear down on them with the whole weight of your body. (The undersides of the rising toes are related to the brain. See Figure 70). Kneel up and down rhythmically, tapping your bottom on the floor as much as you like (this sends energy to the brain).

2. Following the last exercise, rest in the Seisa position, place your hands, palms up, on your thighs and relax for a moment breathing deeply before going on to perform Do-in of the abdomen.

THE ABDOMEN

As might be expected, the abdomen, which is the centre of the body and of the energy spiral, is very important and very rich in diagnostic and therapeutic possibilities. There are three parts in the abdomen, from the most supple part (Yin) at the top to the firmest part (Yang) at the base.

At the top, in the hollow just below the sternum (the breastbone), there is a place which could give easily under the pressure of the fingers. It ought to be soft (negative or Yin). If it is hard, the person's ideas are fixed (see the relationship with the nape of the neck).

The hara, located at three fingers' widths below the navel, should be firm (positive or Yang).

Half-way between the navel and the upper point is another point, and this should strike a balance between its two neighbours on either side, being neither too hard nor too soft. If it is in this 'neutral' condition, your digestion is good.

The state of these three points provides information about your health. Often it is the upper point that is hard (and then the solar plexus, the diaphragm and the nape of the neck are blocked) and it is the lower point that is soft (no hara). The upper part of the abdomen situated in the open triangle towards the base of the rib cage is called the epigastrium. Figure 102b shows that this zone is related to the nape of the neck. It is easy to verify this correspondence because, if the

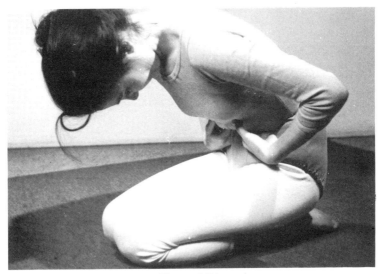

Figure 101.

back of your neck becomes tired during a long drive, the zone in question grows hard and the solar plexus is painful to touch. The zone should be supple and, if it is hard and painful, the nape of the neck must be unblocked. The epigastrium corresponds to the stomach and the heart as far as the body organs are concerned.

Do-in performed on this zone treats:

The stomach: acidity, heartburn, ulcers, aerophagia, bilious attacks.

The heart: this and the whole surrounding part of the thorax are invigorated.

The pancreas: diabetes.

The spleen: composition of the blood, circulation of energy.

Liver, gall bladder.

Kidneys and adrenals that are underactive.

Tension: blockages of the solar plexus and diaphragm.

Figure 102.   Correspondences of the abdomen.

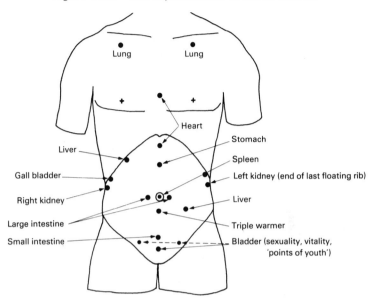

102a. Diagnostic and treatment points.

The Do-in is as follows:

1. Sit in the Seisa position and dig the fingers in under the ribs on each side of the breastbone and exhale while bending over onto the thighs. Remain in this position for as long as you can without straining and then sit back while breathing in.

2. Repeat at least three times (Figure 101).

3. Begin again, moving your fingers more to the outside, towards the waist.

4. Go through the process again, but remain in the bent-over position, breathing gently, and massage underneath your ribs with the tips of your fingers in a circular movement.

5. Sit up straight, place the fingers of your right hand together and press them perpendicularly into the

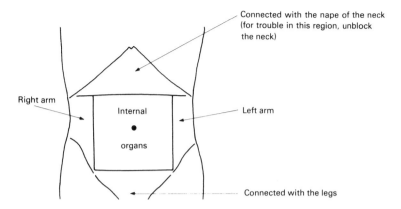

102b. Relationships between the abdomen and the limbs.

abdominal wall over the antecardium, using the left hand to increase the pressure.

6. Using the tips of the fingers of both hands, massage in an up-and-down movement between the sternum and the navel, pressing lightly in the middle axis and trying above all to obtain a warming effect.

7. A particularly effective practice for strengthening the whole body is as follows. Pummel your stomach five hundred times with your fists on rising in the morning, starting gently and continue more and more vigorously, without hurting yourself. The resulting benefits will surprise you.

The Navel

The navel region is connected with the spleen and the intestines. The navel ought to be a regularly shaped hole which should rise slightly. If it sinks the general health is poor, especially in the lower part of the abdomen. If it is drawn in any other direction than upwards, a disease is indicated in that part of the abdomen. If, while breathing out, you push on the navel with the palm of your hand, and feel a pulse beating and the area is hard and painful, this denotes troubles of the spleen and pancreas.

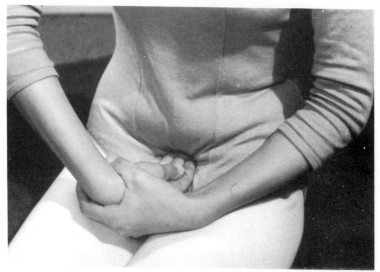

Figure 103.

1. Perform a warming massage with the flat of the hand.

2. Strike gently with the cupped hand.

The Lower Abdomen

The lower abdomen is mainly linked with the sexual organs and the urinary passages. Therefore, it is an important centre in the diagnosis and treatment of the vital energy. Sexual energy is in fact the source and root of life. When sexual energy is burnt out, senility and death are not far away. There is an important corresponding point called for this reason, the 'point of youth', above the pubic bone at the level of the bladder.

1. In order to treat it, place the fingers of the right hand together and press them perpendicularly into the lower abdomen using the left hand to push the right one (Figure 103).

2. Do the same with both hands and press on the right, left and centre simultaneously, towards the groin.

Massage of the Abdomen

1. Stretch out on the floor and start to massage your abdomen in the (spiral) direction followed by the intestines.

2. Place the flattened fingertips of the right hand above your navel; lightly place your left hand on it and, while performing rotary massage, move down towards your bladder, turn right, return up the ascending colon, cross the abdomen between the navel and the stomach, directly over the transverse colon, and descend again on the left along the descending colon to the pubes. Press well on the zone above the pubes to get rid of intestinal gas.

Hara Exercises

In practising Do-in, we have followed the body spiral right round until our final massage of the abdomen's own spiral. We shall now proceed to intensify the *hara*, which is the centre of this spiral, and concentrate energy at this point. There are many exercises available for intensifying and strengthening the hara. Here we shall suggest three that are simple but very effective.

1. Lie on your back with your legs slightly apart and your arms along your body. Breathe in deeply and, while breathing out suddenly through your mouth and concentrating all your attention on the hara, start to sit up while at the same time pulling your arms forwards between your legs. The arms must be turned outwards so that your hands are back to back (Figure 104). This concentrates the effort at the centre of the body (try it the other way round and you will feel the dispersal of effort).

2. Repeat this exercise as often as you like.

3. Carry out the above movement while at the same time bringing your feet, soles together, towards your pelvis.

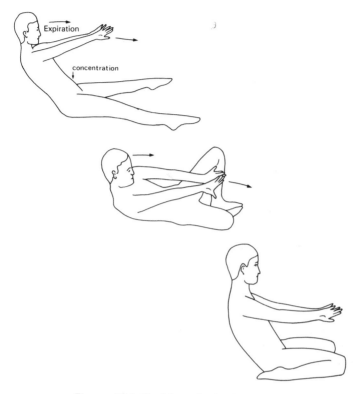

Figure 104. Positions for hara exercises.

4. If you are not suffering from kidney trouble (lumbago, sciatica), carry out the final exercise. The initial position is the following: sit in the Seisa pose and separate your feet so that you can sit with your buttocks resting on the floor; stretch backwards and pull yourself up again as indicated in the preceding exercises.

Generally speaking, it is better to keep to the second exercise — the nearer you bring your feet to the crotch, the more effective it is. You will find in this exercise that the effort is much more intense lower down, at the level of the internal sexual organs and in the crotch; hence it is especially recommended for women.

THE BACK

The back is the noblest part of our body. Man has sometimes been said to be divided between God and the Devil, with God represented by the back and the Devil by the abdomen with its viscera and sexual organs. In the back, the vertebral column is like an electronic keyboard, from which commands are relayed to all parts of the body (see Figure 3 showing the meridians in the back). When a given vertebra is damaged, the corresponding organ and function suffer. Conversely, if an organ functions badly (by overeating for example), the corresponding vertebra becomes jammed, and painful zones appear in the back. The back also reflects our

Figure 105.

mental life; it registers all the tensions, all the conflicts, all the stress, translating them into muscular knots and tensions; the consequence being a poor circulation of energy and organic troubles.

Therefore it is important to have a perfectly healthy back. Later on we shall be looking at some supplementary correction exercises designed to rebuild a strong back. Earlier, I showed you Do-in techniques for massaging the entire backbone and the accompanying meridians: the governing vessel (one of the eight 'Special Meridians' of acupuncture) and bladder meridians. We shall complete this massage by warming the whole back.

1. This back-warming is copied from animals. Rub the back and kidney region on the ground as energetically as possible, and move about in any direction you feel is beneficial and warming.

Figure 106.

2. In order to increase the effect in the 'awkward zone', raise your arms with your hands clasped and stretch them upwards while rolling from right to left, raise your bottom well clear of the ground so that you are supported only on your heels and your back and push the hara up (Figure 105).

3. Continue by doing the movement inversely, placing your lumbar region on the floor, transmitting your weight through it and massaging this area of your back against the floor (Figure 106).

4. Finish by swinging from side to side to get maximum warmth by friction on the carpet. This method can be practised when you feel cold in the back as it is excellent for overcoming chills.

Relaxation

1. Following this fine warming massage, stretch to your fullest extent, push out your arms and legs as far as possible from your body and then gradually contract your body as much as you can, while breathing out.

2. Gradually release the tension while breathing in.

3. Repeat at least three times. After the maximum degree of tension (Yang), the relaxation (Yin) comes automatically and completely.

4. Rest stretched out where you are, with your legs straight and slightly separated, your toes turned out, your arms lying beside your body, a little separated with their hands turned up, and hold your head straight, your teeth unclenched and your lips just parted.

5. Allow your breathing to settle down to a quiet, steady rate. This relaxation permits a free circulation of the energy and encourages the effects of the Do-in to harmonize with one another.

6. Rest for as long as you wish.

7. Before getting up, gently stretch yourself once more, and then roll from one side to the other. When you are lying on your right side bring your knees up to your chest and roll back into the sitting, Seisa, position, extended over your thighs with your head on your knees and your hands laid flat in front

of your knees. Rest a moment like this, breathing deeply and forcing the respiration into the back and kidneys.

8. Rise quietly into the Seisa position, with your back very straight and the nape of your neck and your head in line with your back, your hands on your thighs, their palms up or clasped with the left hand in the right hand, the thumbs linked.

Chants

1. When in this position carry out an internal Do-in in which the massage is done with vibrating sounds.

2. Calmly pronounce the vowels A – E – I – O – U

   A – concentrate on the level of the face.
   E – lungs and heart.
   I – stomach, liver, pancreas, spleen, waist.
   O – abdomen, intestines, hara.
   U – sexual organs.

3. Repeat at least three times and then pronounce the word 'Om'. This consists of a low-pitched 'O' starting in the abdomen and rising steadily until it ends in a hummed 'M'.

Yoga

After you have performed your morning Do-in, more or less thoroughly according to the time at your disposal or the need you feel for it, you can continue:

1. With breathing exercises if you have done none during your Do-in session. These breathing exercises are just as effective if they are left to the end. Do what you think best.

2. With a session of hatha yoga and, in particular with the sun greetings (see traditional Hindu yoga).

3. With corrective exercises such as the basic ones we are going to suggest in the following section.

4. By going for a walk.

Strong, Supple Back

Stretching the Body
We should learn how to stretch ourselves, because one's development in life depends on expansion.

Our environment tends to cramp and compress us, and so we ought to enjoy a good stretch to give our joints free play and to permit the free circulation of energy.

Stretching on the Rib Stall
If you do not have the use of a gymnastic rib stall, make do with a ladder, a tree-branch or a wall. A bar is to be preferred so that you can get a good grip.

1. Hang by your hands, with both of them at the same level. The first thing to aim for is a state of relaxation in this suspended position. Such relaxation is not always immediate. What usually happens in the beginning is that the body is contracted due to fear or to a lack of strength in the hands. So at first you should content yourself with simply hanging there to develop your manual strength and to acquire a good grip (Figure 107).

2. If you find that you can stay there for several minutes without tiring, try to relax your body. Only

Figure 107.

the hands must be contracted (Mazda yoga); all the
rest of the body, shoulders, back, legs and feet,
must be slack and your thighs and lower legs must
be like those of a rag doll. It will take a number of
sessions to achieve this state properly but, once it
comes naturally to you, you can start breathing
deeply at the same time. You may well find,
however, that breathing is a little difficult.

3. So, as soon as your body is fully relaxed, you should
   take a deep breath. At that moment you will feel
   your pelvis descend an inch or so. Breathe out again
   and your pelvis will rise. Take another deep breath
   and so on.

In this way, you will obtain a natural rhythmic stretching
of the whole spinal column and limbs. It is obvious that this
practice is particularly effective for freeing the vertebrae. It
also treats the other joints — the wrists, elbows, shoulders,
hips, knees and ankles. Do this exercise during your physical
training periods, after any strenuous effort and, in particular,
in the evening before going to bed. It will release you from
the cramped habits of the day and your sleep will be more
beneficial since the energy will circulate freely throughout
your body.

Stretching and Twisting

1. Sit on a chair back to front, that is to say facing the
   back and with your legs on either side (Figure 108).

2. Sit up straight and, breathing in deeply, raise one
   arm as high as you can while pressing it tight
   against your head. and bend over sideways, away
   from the raised arm. Breathe out as you bend over
   and keep your back nice and flat. Keep your
   stomach in and breathe in as you straighten up
   again — then change sides (Figure 109).

3. Repeat the exercise as often as you like but at least
   three times for each side.

4. Do the same thing with your lungs full, without
   forcing. This exercise mobilizes the lumbar

vertebrae in a corrective fashion (and loosens the fifth lumbo-sacral vertebra (treatment of the sciatic nerves).

5. Do the same movement with your arms clasped behind your back, one arm coming from over its own shoulder and the other up from below on the other side to meet it, as indicated in the Do-in

Figure 108.

Figure 109.

lessons (Figure 110). New flexibility is then imparted to the 'awkward zone' between your shoulder blades.

6. While still sitting up straight, twist your trunk to right and left, helping yourself by holding the chair, but do not strain. Breathe out during the twist, hold the position for a moment and then breathe in gently (Figure 111).

Development of the Front of the Body

1. Place a rolled up blanket on a stool or box, or throw a folded rug over a tree-trunk or a barrel if you have one.

2. Now lie back on this support. That is to say, place the lower part of your back and kidney region on the rug, your feet on the ground and, while breathing slowly, let the top part of your body fall gently backwards. Your arms and head will descend gently under their own weight (passive work) and by the free motion of respiration and the relaxation of the front of the body. The stretching can be increased if you hold a weight of 2 to 5 lbs (1-2 kg) in your hands (Figure 112).

Figure 110.

3. Relax as you breathe and the abdominal muscles will slacken little by little, your solar plexus will be stretched, the rib cage will open out and the entire cardiac zone will be cleared.

The passive work and warming of the back in this exercise ensures beneficial results. Much of our work is done in a sitting position, hunched forward — a habit we learn as soon as we start school. This exercise is designed to counteract that bad posture. It strengthens the functions of the heart and liver; the circulation of blood in the abdomen and chest is stimulated if it is poor, and elimination is thereby improved. Also the sexual functions are assisted.

Exercising in the Prone Position
Stretch out, face down, on the floor with your legs together, your abdomen retracted, your spine and neck in line, your chin tucked in and your face lifted off the ground. Rest your weight on your legs and thighs and on the upper part of your chest — not on the lower chest as that would throw the lumbar region out of line (Figure 113). Carry out the following contractions as thoroughly as possible:

1. Contract the anus; draw in your buttocks as if you were trying to make them pass between your legs and press your pubic region against the floor;

Figure 111.

2. Contract your abdomen (the hara) and pull it in towards your spine;

3. Tuck your chin in, squeezing your throat.

Hold this position for a while. It makes very good orthopaedic sense and increases energy. In fact, the above three contractions bring about a perfect concentration of energy: the excretory energy in the lower region of the body is sent to the centre by the contraction of the anus; the closing of the valve near the tip of the sternum prevents any energy escaping upwards; and respiratory energy descends and is compressed with the digestive energy at the focal point of the concave diaphragm, or in the hara which you are also compressing. If you make sure that you concentrate on your hara throughout the exercise, you can carry out several series of compressions without suffering from any fatigue.

Figure 112.

1. Raise your arms and spread them out to make a cross-formation with your body, clenching your fists with your palms facing the ground. Stretch your arms as far as possible in front of you in line with your back (do not let the lumbar region cave in). Now, starting from that position and breathing in, bring your arms back along your body and keep them as high as possible, while turning your fists so

as to bring the backs of the hands to face one another (your shoulder blades will stay close to your back).

2. Breathe out while bringing your arms back to the front.

3. Rest your arms on the floor, relax and breathe calmly.

4. Begin the exercise again and, as soon as you have perfectly mastered the position, perform the exercise several times without resting your arms.

5. Then breathe in slowly during a certain number of backwards and forwards movements and breathe out again during the same number of movements.

6. Do not force your body to work; start gently and wait for your heart and lungs to gain strength day by day.

This exercise is far from being merely a corrective exercise for the back muscles. It stimulates the whole body by the energy recharge in the spinal column and the muscular work done by the entire body from the soles of the feet to the roots of the hair. It has many effects: the kidneys, adrenal glands, sexual functions, heart and lungs are strengthened and all trace of dyspepsia, indigestion and intestinal gases disappears. If you practice it every morning, you will feel relaxed and contented. It will rid you of neurasthenia (because of the warming work on top of the back and the nape of the neck).

Strengthening the Lumbar Region

Lying prone:

1. Adopt exactly the same position as before.

2. Place your fists on your pelvis with your palms turned towards the floor.

3. Lift one leg, keeping it nice and straight with the foot held square and stretch your Achilles tendon to the maximum without bending your knee.

4. The leg and foot resting on the floor, turned outwards — this will keep your pelvis flat on the ground, ensuring the effectiveness of the exercise (Figure 114). Due to this position, your other leg will not be able to rise very high, but the work done is very intense on and around the quadrate muscle in the loins.

5. Concentrate your attention on the kidneys.

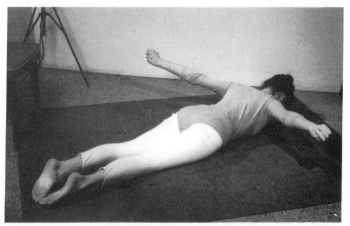

Figure 113.

Figure 114.

6. Repeat this exercise with alternate legs and then with both legs raised together.

This exercise strengthens the kidneys and quickly benefits lumbago and sciatica. It regulates the intestinal functions (constipation, gas) and massages the kidneys, pancreas, spleen and liver. Ptoses of the stomach and of the other visceral organs (the kidneys especially) are corrected. The circulation in the chest is improved and the heart and lungs are fortified. Decisiveness of mind is stimulated and the individual becomes more active.

Figure 115.

When seated:

1. Sit down cross-legged, interlock your fingers and raise your arms to the ceiling with the palms of your hands upwards.

2. Stretch your trunk as much as possible in an upwards direction and push with your hands as if trying to lift the sky (Figure 115).

3. Repeat this exercise several times without worrying about your respiration, and try to make your back straight and to push your hands as high as possible with head erect.

4. When this first part of the exercise has been mastered, start again while inhaling deeply and then, on exhaling, contract all parts of your body, especially your trunk and arms. Then gradually relax the tension while inhaling again. Let your arms fall down and breathe deeply. Repeat three to seven times.

This exercise corrects the back and tones up the heart and visceral organs. It also treats rheumatism of the shoulders and helps to recharge nervous energy.

On the plank:

1. Take a board about 6 ft (2m approx.) long and lean it against a bed, a chair or one of the first rungs of a rib stall at an angle of about 30°.

2. Stretch yourself along it with your head at the bottom (Figure 116). It is a good idea to fasten yourself to the board to make sure you stay in place. Pass a broad rubber strap round your hips, make a flat knot behind the pelvis and tie the two loose ends to the top of the board.

This ensures that the lumbar region lies flush on the board and your body is held in suspension by the strap. Do not

Figure 116.

pass the strap round your waist or it will cut off the circulation and interfere with abdominal respiration. Make sure that the strap crosses the hips just above the joints of the thighs. You should spread your legs a little on the board so that you do not slip through the rubber strap.

By tying the strap behind you, you allow your kidney area to lie flat on the board. if you knot it in front over your abdomen, your lumbar region will tend to hollow out. Also, the long ends of the strap will be liable to cut into the groin. Relax in this position, breathe slowly and rest there for at least fifteen minutes.

This exercise has the following effects:

1. It stretches the whole spinal column and the lumbar zone in particular. It is this zone that supports the whole weight of the body when we are standing or working. The lower the vertebrae are when we are in the normal, erect position, the more they will benefit from the pull of the body's weight when the normal position is reversed.

2. The back and the nape of the neck are also extended and one should take the opportunity to move the back and neck to right and left and to rotate them. You will feel the vertebrae being freed.

This exercise offers the advantages of a yoga head-stand without any risk to the vertebrae. Those with an imperfect vertebral column can sometimes suffer from spinal deformation and crushing if they try to stand on their heads. Here is a short reminder of the benefits to be obtained from this upside-down position. It aids the return of dark blood from legs and abdomen to the lungs, and this relieves congestion and purifies the viscera. On the other hand, it also helps fresh blood to reach the brain. With the improvement of the blood circulation in the head, the pituitary gland, which controls the hormones, functions better. The functioning of the organs is also invigorated. This exercise is of immense value in helping the body recuperate from nervous fatigue and, once completed the whole body (especially your head) will feel refreshed; your thinking will become clear and you will be ready to enjoy whatever the evening has in store.

To sum up, this pose treats headaches, insomnia, indigestion, nervous irritation, a stiff neck, stomach ache, haemorrhoids (piles), troubles of the prostate gland, prolapse of various organs etc. But it is essential to practise it two times a day, for fifteen minutes in the morning and fifteen minutes around five o'clock in the afternoon, and not near mealtimes. It is also a particularly effective treatment for renal colic. When the crisis occurs it eases the pain by supplying energy and draining the kidneys. In general, it stimulates the circulation in the kidneys and helps elimination. Eye, nose and throat troubles rapidly disappear. The memory and mental capacities are improved, neurasthenia relieved and mental agitation settles down — hence the pose is especially recommended before a meditation session.

After you have spent fifteen minutes on the board, slip your legs through the rubber strap and slide gently to the floor. Lie there without stirring for at least two or three minutes; *never get up suddenly*, even if the phone or doorbell rings!

One advantage that resting on the board has over certain yoga asanas such as *Shirshasana* (head-stand) and *Sarvangasana* (shoulder-stand), is that one can, at the same time, perform Do-in of the head, face, neck, chest and abdomen. During the fifteen minutes you can massage your chest and do deep breathing as a preparation for *Pranayama. Uddiyana Bandha* (retraction of the abdomen) and *Nauli* exercises may also be profitably performed in this position. The physical and mental effects of these practices added to the benefits of the upside-down pose are really miraculous.

PART THREE

ENERGY CYCLES

RHYTHMS OF LIFE

In this section we are going to show how man vibrates to the rhythm of cosmic energy. The reader will understand why his body is a spiral of energy in the image of the galaxy. He will then be convinced that practising Do-in in the direction of the flow of this energy will tend to put him in harmony with the cosmic rhythm. Consequently he will live more happily on all levels — physical, mental and spiritual.

By looking at one or two aspects of human life, we shall discover how this universal rhythm shows itself in the ancient and modern rules of life throughout the world. First of all we shall examine the daily life of mankind, with its basic problems of physical health.

The Daily Cycle

This is the simplest and one of the most important cycles. It is obviously broken up into day (activity — Yang) and night (rest — Yin).

Two phases are important in human physiology: assimilation and elimination. It is very important for these functions to take place in the respective organs just when the energy in these organs is at its maximum. When the last meal has long been over and assimilation is finished, the elimination phase takes over.

The elimination phase is disagreeable to people who are congested. They feel tired and irritable. But as soon as they start eating again, the elimination phase ceases and, because the energy is increased as digestion takes place,

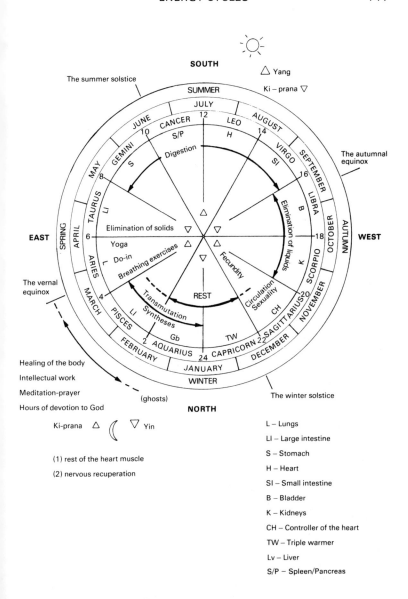

Figure 117. Energy cycles.

they regain their good humour. This is the phenomenon of 'false hunger'. When a person is clogged, food acts like a drug; by abusing it he continues to clog his body by constantly hindering elimination.

The condition in which you wake up in the morning has great diagnostic value. It is a long time since you have had a meal and so elimination is in full operation. If you are in fine fettle it is because your body is clean; if you are headachy, lazy and growling like a bear with a sore head, the reason is that your body is overloaded with waste materials and you are in the process of trying to eliminate them. However, as soon as you have a cup of tea or settle down to breakfast, the elimination phase comes to a halt and you start to feel cheerful — you have disguised your problem, which will reappear later on in the form of an illness. Therefore the ideal plan is not to eat during the morning, because then elimination is prolonged from the seven o'clock supper until noon on the following day, for a period of seventeen hours. This constitutes the daily fast. Every day must be sufficient in itself: assimilation and elimination should balance out, the ideal being the elimination each day of the toxins accumulated the day before.

The daily Energy Cycle indicates that one should eat no more than once a day, the best time being between 10 a.m. and 12 noon. Iranians back in the days of the great Persian Empire ate only once a day and were extremely hardy. Tibetan monks take no more solid nourishment after noon. Carthusian monks have their main meal around midday and a very light vegetable soup in the evening. Socrates said that those who eat more than twice a day are barbarians.

In *The Gospel of the Peace of Jesus Christ by the Disciple John* (Edmond Székely's adaptation of ancient Aramaic and Slavonic texts, ed. Pierre Genillard, Lausanne) we read:

> Eat only when the sun is at its highest point in the sky and a second time when it has set. Then you will never see illness, for those who do thus find favour in the eyes of the Lord. And if you would have the angels of God to take delight in your body and would like Satan to flee far from you, then take your place only once a day at the table of God.

Victor Hugo wrote:

> Get up at six
> And dine at ten
> Then sup at six
> Retire at ten
> And you will live to ten times ten.

These are exactly the hours when the energy circulates freely around all the organs. There is no need to eat a lot. Eating a little is, in one way, eating a lot, because the body is able to assimilate the food better. What counts is not what one eats but what one assimilates. Thorough mastication is of prime importance (see the section on Do-in of the mouth). The more food one puts in the mouth, the less one can eat. Mastication charges the food with energy, which is then absorbed in maximum amounts.

We have to talk in terms of energy because everything is energy. Our solid food is concentrated energy that forms the vehicle for a large quantity of more subtle energy. Man himself is energy, and energy is therefore the final goal of the process of assimilation. You should place less and less reliance on material nourishment and should train yourself to increase your direct intake of energy little by little by means of exercise, respiration, yoga, Do-in and meditation.

The response of our bodies to overeating is to weaken the functions of assimilation and, if we persist with this bad habit, our bodies will allow the organs of assimilation to function badly and so impede the input of energy. The worst of all physiological states is *an excess of energy*. It lies at the root of all diseases. Everything which exceeds the quantity we can use generates waste products which accumulate in the organism and interfere with the proper functioning of the organs, causing obesity, constipation, uric acid deposits (with such consequences as arthritis, rheumatism and arteriosclerosis), fermentation in the intestines, infection of the organs of elimination (kidneys, liver, lungs, genito-urinary organs).

Furthermore, the chemical breakdown of a large quantity of food entails a big expenditure of energy. The heavy eater is always tired and off-colour, and so he eats increasingly rich foods to try and make up for the deficiency in the organs of assimilation, which the body has 'called out on strike'. There is then a tendency to try to stimulate these organs to act by the use of spices etc. It is a vicious circle and the only way the body has of breaking out of it is to create some disease such as a stomach ulcer or liver trouble. Hunger is a necessity at all times and if you will accept hunger as your companion you will always be cheerful and in good form. People generally like to go about stuffed with food (out of fear, the need for security and to be certain they have had enough); nevertheless you should adopt the habit of living with an edge on your appetite and of not being afraid. Appetite is a source of joy. Work up a really good appetite by working hard and do not ever completely satisfy it with the food you eat; all your other appetites — intellectual, artistic, sexual, etc — will then become greater. You can obtain this result by decreasing the number of your meals and the amount eaten at each meal. Never eat until you are completely full.

Deny yourself all good that is not absolutely indispensable (remembering that sometimes an excess is indispensable for mental reasons). With a full stomach you will no longer have the energy to be enterprising and adventurous. Keep busy and do not think about food; it is idleness that leads to excess and self-indulgence. The worst thing of all is to eat when you are not hungry as this sows the seeds of every disease. Skip as many meals as required to achieve true hunger.

To experience hunger each day is the golden rule of health and the source of joy and justice. It is the proof that you have reached the end of the elimination phase belonging to the preceding stage of assimilation and that the day's cycle is complete. All this is essential on the physiological level, but it goes much further than that.

We ought to live in the realization that we are linked with the universe as a whole. When, we may ask, is man at his most egotistical and most inward looking? The answer is, when he is eating and digesting. It is essential to have an empty stomach for as long as possible in order to be free to turn towards the world, to be able to give (massage, laying on of hands, intellectual work, meditation, contact with our fellows). Hunger prolongs, reinforces and improves the quality of life (as indicated by numerous systematic experiments on rats). While we remain hungry for physical food, we are nourishing our etheric body, which then has to take from the atmosphere the principles it needs. This stimulates it and it takes a more active part in our life. Nor should it be forgotten that the Subtle Energy (the Spirit and the Soul) animates the matter which has been committed to its care and is used by it to make its way through life, matter which dies physically when it can no longer serve the Spirit.

Since the daily cycle is the most important one, it is the cycle which requires our main attention. We shall touch on the other cycles more briefly, but sufficiently to help the reader understand that life is vibration and that wisdom consists in falling into step with these vibrations, so that we are helped along by them so to speak.

The Weekly Cycle

The harmonies are as follows:

Day	Correspondence	Period	Food
Tuesday	autumn		
Wednesday Thursday	winter	Yin	Yang, restorative, temperate
Friday	spring		fast day
Saturday Sunday	summer	Yang	Yin, more varied and tasty
Monday	end of summer		

Table 1. The weekly cycle and its correspondences.

The period from Monday to Thursday is one of serious, concentrated activities; it corresponds to north and winter and peaks on Wednesday (December). If you intend to organize a spiritual meeting or a meditation session, arrange them for Wednesday evening, for then spiritual activity reaches its high point. On Thursday activity has already begun to slow down. Friday corresponds to spring and is a day for fasting. On Saturday and Sunday, the 'atmosphere' becomes warmer (Yang); the tone is less serious, it becomes more southern in character, happier and more high-lighted.

If you want to see a comedy, go to the cinema on Saturday night not during the early part of the week. Use Sundays for your dinner parties and epicurean meals, they will go down better than on a weekday. A fast on Friday is a most salutary habit which will give your organs a rest. If you prefer another day, choose Monday. Always stick to the same day. It is important to initiate a rhythm; regularity (and moderation in all things) brings health and endurance. Avoid any breaks in the rhythm of your life.

N.B. This does not exclude the possibility of throwing the occasional memorable party — these can be good for both body and mind.

The Monthly Cycle

This corresponds approximately to the lunations and is also intensively studied now in the form of biorhythms. Readers who would like further information should turn to specialized books on these subjects.* We shall content ourselves with giving the cycles.

Tissue	Structures	Cycle (in days)
the ectoderm	nervous system	33-day
the mesoderm	bones and muscles	23-day
the endoderm	digestive tract, sexual organs	28-day

Table 2. The length of the cycles of the structures developed from the three embryological tissues.

During the active period which is represented by one half of a cycle, the period corresponding to day (Yang), you can exert your energy to the maximum as it is then turned outwards. In the other half of a cycle, the period is passive (Yin) and corresponds to night. You should then take things more quietly, as your body is at rest, recuperating, and enriching itself (not only through regeneration of the tissues

*Biorhythms by Peter West, published by Thorsons Publishers Limited, Denington Estate, Wellingborough, Northants.

but also through meditation). You should especially notice those days when the active phases change over to the passive ones. On such days the body is fully preoccupied with the change and you need to be very careful; for example, avoid driving your car, because there is a great chance of an accident. If you study books about these lunar cycles and the nodes of the moon you will find that there is the same balance between rest and activity as there is between Yin and Yang. It is very interesting and instructive. You will see how easy it is to relate all the rules of agriculture (sowing, tree pruning, etc ...) to the waxing and waning of the moon.

The Annual Cycle

With a view to bringing together the ideas of East and West, we shall present the Yin-Yang philosophy alongside Celtic tradition. The Celts, also, could see harmonies between the cycles of a day, a year and a life. Their day commenced at sunset at the end of the previous day. During the night, the sleeping man relaxes his muscles and nerves, puts his organic functions in order and renews his mental and physical powers ready for the activities of the coming day.

In the same way, all existence commences at the hour of death, the moment which marks the termination of the preceding existence. The end of life is followed by a phase of rest to which the active phase of another life will succeed. During the resting phase, the man, or rather the energy corresponding to him is nourished and regenerated, so the Celts believed, by cosmic forces.

The Celtic year begins on the 1st November (the day of the dead), which marks the close of the preceding year and the beginning of the dark months (November and December). During this dark period, inactive nature draws from the universe those cosmic forces which, as soon as the winter solstice is past (Christmas), will allow her to resume her ten month's effort in the vegetable kingdom: germination, putting forth the tender shoot, budding, flowering, branching, seeding, ripening, harvesting, sowing, shedding leaves, death, decay, rest, germination and so on. It is the same for animals and men. We should be forced to repeat ourselves if we were to deal with the Celtic and Eastern points of view separately, since they obviously have a similar view of the universe.

The annual cycle of the seasons is the image of a day (Figure 117). The hot summer corresponds to day and is Yang, while the winter corresponds to night and is Yin. Spring is the dawn of the year and autumn its dusk. Taking the daily cycle as a pattern, we can deduce our activities and our problems through a year by analogy. We shall give merely a few examples by way of demonstration.

In winter there are no more fruits or fresh vegetables and we eat what we have been able to preserve, such as roots, cereals, beans, dried fruit and animal products. Such food is Yang and very rich. It is generally cooked and enriched by the vibrations from the fire and so it is suitable for combating the cold (Yin) of winter. When spring arrives, man is still under the influence of the nourishment he has absorbed during winter (the influence of nourishment lasts for at least four months). The climate then warms up, and we are relatively too Yang – too charged with Yang energy accumulated in winter. We are often further poisoned by the sedentary life of the winter months. If nature is working as she should, spring is the period of maximum elimination (just as the morning is a time of elimination in the daily cycle) and our bodies are working inside at maximum intensity. What is more, what has been harvested and stored is practically exhausted, the quantity of food is reduced (this is a period for fasting in all religions) and plenty of hard work is required to cultivate the soil (you should engage in hard physical work in the morning on an empty stomach to eliminate waste matter and fortify your health).

The same is true of the entire world around us. In the dawn of the year, life is still interior for it is still winter, but a great upheaval is going on beneath the soil; the corn is germinating unseen, all appears to be quiescent, but the vegetable kingdom is in vigorous activity beneath the surface. Then, in March, April and May, its forces are turned outwards and the plants sprout and grow. Birds are in full song and mate and multiply. Man too becomes very animated and active. He starts to eat well again. It is the end of Lent.

Then the hot summer days arrive with all the abundance

of good things nature supplies. This is the time of maturity. Because of the great heat, man eats fresher foodstuffs (Yin) and adopts a lighter diet consisting of fruits, vegetables and, in general, he prefers raw to cooked food; he consumes less animal products and less salt, but drinks more liquids.

When autumn comes, man is still under the influence of this Yin diet of summer and is too Yin for the cold, damp weather, and so he falls an easy victim to colds and flu, especially as the energy is at its low point in the lungs during this period. It is wise, therefore, to undergo a fast in order to eliminate the effects of summer eating habits, and that is why all religions impose a new period of fasting at this time. Furthermore, autumn is the period when the active phase changes over to the passive phase. By comparing this with what happens in the biorhythms (the monthly cycle) and the cycle of life (the start of retirement) one can see that special care should be taken of the health during this period (September).

I will leave to you the pleasure of discovering and pursuing all the various comparisons one can make between the various cycles. However, here is a summary of the example we have just studied:

DAILY CYCLE		ANNUAL CYCLE	
Phase	**Comment**	**Phase**	**Comment**
Evening	Meal optional — though better not to eat. Watch your health — wrap up at nightfall (lungs).	Autumn	A fast desirable in this period. Watch your health (lungs).
Night	Sleep	Winter	Dark time — rest.
Morning	Fast (for liver). Physical activity.	Spring	Fast (for liver). Much activity.
Afternoon	Main meal. Activity.	Summer	Abundance of food. Activity.

Table 3. Comparison between the phases of the daily cycle and the phases of the annual cycle.

The Cycles of Energy in Life

To begin with, life goes through a great oscillation between Yang (active) and Yin (passive). Life starts with its spring (infancy) then goes on to summer (maturity). These two periods are very active, but then it descends to its autumn (the start of retirement) and goes on into old age until death (All Saints' Day when the dead are commemorated), when human energy enters its long night (winter) to recharge itself and to await a new birth (Christmas, the Nativity).

Just as in the daily cycle, the assimilation phase dominates the first half of life. Man is in full growth on all levels until he reaches the peak of maturity and starts to decline. In the first part of life all sorts of food should be eaten, and the infant, in particular, must eat everything the earth provides in order to discover it. Nevertheless, this rule is modified by a longer-term rhythm than can be encompassed within a single life. Those who believe in reincarnation would regard this rhythm as due to the passage from life to life; those who do not would explain it in terms of heredity. Anyway, what we may call 'young souls' need to be omnivorous like a small child, whereas 'old souls' ought to be vegetarians like a person of mature age or like an old person.

In the monthly cycle (biorhythms), as we have seen, there is a critical day when the active phase changes over to the passive phase; a day when it is wise to exercise care. In the same way, retirement is often taken very badly by many people, and they quickly fall ill or even die. On the other hand, given time, the retired are able to enter a happier period.

During the second half of life, the elimination phase takes over from assimilation and, by referring to the daily cycle, you will be able to see what has to be done to prevent disease and to retard the onset of senility. This is the time when one should turn more and more to a vegetarian diet while, at the same time, eating less and less. The life after death should engage his attention and he should prepare for it by nourishing himself more and more on the Ki energy taken directly. Finally, just before death, earthly food should be given up if possible, so that the being can freely enter into the cosmos (see the lives of the great saints).

For this reason, the practice of Do-in is of paramount importance for the elderly, because it prepares them for this direct intake of cosmic energy.

However, a single life also includes lesser cycles. Our cells renew themselves over a period of seven years, at which time the individual passes under the influence of another planet. These seven-year periods are as follows:

Period (in years)	Planet
0–7	Moon
7–14	Venus
14–21	Sun
21–42	Mars

Table 4. Planetary influence in each seven-year cycle.

Every three-times-seven years we cross a threshold:

Period (in years)	Phase
0–21	growth
21–42	full activity
at 63	the beginning of old age

Table 5. Corresponding phase of each triple cycle period.

Actually, these periods are only approximate. To be more accurate, the cycle in women lasts seven years and in men it lasts eight years. This is because the cells renew themselves more rapidly in women, as the composition of their blood is different:

Haemoglobin (mg/100 c.c. blood)	Red Corpuscles (million/mm³)
Male 16	5 – 5.2
Female 14	4.4 – 4.6

Table 6. Composition of blood in men and women.

Official medicine advises us that our food should contain the following number of calories:

for women – 2800 calories/day
for men   – 3200 calories/day

These quantities are disputed by some schools of medicine which propose the following figures:

for women – 1400 calories/day
for men   – 1600 calories/day

So in women the cycles run for seven years, with three and a half years turned outwards (activities, talents) and with three and a half years turned inwards (enrichment). It is assumed that the cycles commence at an age when the infant becomes truly autonomous for the first time and stands upright (in the typically human attitude for the reception of cosmic energy – see below on the Galactic Cycle), but the calculation can also be made from the date of birth if preferred:

Cycle			Years			
Women:						
		1	8	15	22	29
	or	0	7	14	21	28
Men:						
		1	9	17	25	33
	or	0	8	16	24	32

Table 7. Progression of the cycles in men and women.

This is important to know because these cycles play a part in the life of married couples. For example, at twenty-nine the wife will enter an active phase for three and a half years, while her husband, if he was born in the same year as her, will enter a passive period for four years. Now, if she is already dominant by nature while he is fairly docile, a point may be reached where she pushes him around too much and makes demands he is unable to satisfy. The result may be a breakdown in the marriage and even divorce due to the unhappiness and turmoil involved. But if they realize how the laws of the universe are working in their lives, the weak man will accept that he is now in a period of even greater dependence on a strong woman and the woman will respect his position and refrain from taking advantage of him. They can then come through happily.

The Cycle of Reincarnation

In the course of successive incarnations, there are active lives and passive lives. Some men are very talented, full of possibilities in many fields of endeavour, but do nothing with their lives because they are in a passive life (analogy with night, the passive phase in biorhythms, the passive phases in life.) Such men are preparing for an active future life; it would be useless to make them do something with their present life, just as it is useless and indeed harmful to force a child to pay more attention to his schoolwork during the passive, nervous phase of his biorhythms. During such a life, as during the winter with plants, the seeds of future action are ripening in the bosom of the individual.

Our karmic inheritance has a significant bearing on our choice of food. This is why a given diet can succeed with one person but not with another. It is a mistake to be sectarian on the subject of diet, each one has to find the right balance of foods for himself.

Ages and Civilizations

In the light of the history of past centuries and civilizations, it is possible to tell what will happen in the centuries to come. All that need be done is to apply the Yin-Yang principle which can be expressed more explicitly in the following laws:

1. *The principle of impermanence:* everything that begins will end, and everything will be changed into its opposite.

2. *The principle of back and front:* every front has a back, every coin has both head and tail.

3. *The principle of non-identity:* there are no two

things, two beings, two phenomena in the universe which are identical.

4. *The principle of balance:* the bigger the face the bigger the back.

5. *The principle of polarity:* any change and any process of change is the result of an interaction between two antagonistic forces, the centrifugal Yin force and the centripetal Yang force.

6. *The principle of complementarity:* all antagonisms are complementary as Yin and Yang are complementary.

7. *The principle of unity:* Yin and Yang are the two arms of the ONE, the infinite, constant, limitless and omnipresent ONE.

In Table 8 I give a few indications of the evolution of civilization.

The Galactic Cycle

The most important cycle in which we are involved is that of our own galaxy. All the other cycles are harmoniously derived from this and the simple examination of the galactic cycle will allow us to rediscover and to explain all that we have noted in regard to the preceding sub-cycles. I will give one or two examples, first of all by reverting to the geological eras:

Era	Dominant Life	Period in Years
quaternary	man	1,000,000
tertiary	mammals	60,000,000
secondary	reptiles (and ammonites)	125,000,000
primary	fish (and trilobites)	350,000,000
precambrian	few traces of life bacteria)	3,000,000,000

Table 9, showing dominant life in and length of time of the geological periods.

Seasons	Ages	Health	Nourishment	Functions	Faculties	Civilizations
Spring	birth	fragility (baby)	from the mother	Assimilation (growth)	mechanical sensory	prehistory
Summer	childhood	growth	from the whole earth		sentimental	Mediaeval chivalry (heart)
	adulthood	intellectual and physical maturity	beginning of vegetarianism		intellectual	present-day civilizations scientific research
					social	social revolutions
			full vegetarianism		ideological	
60 years						
Autumn	retreat	physical decline	integral	Elimination (purification)		
		spiritual development				
	1st old age	senility	vegetarianism and spiritual nourishment (Ki)			illnesses
Winter	great old age (wise men, Hunzas Ecuador, The Urals)	wisdom			supreme	numerous deaths
						reduction in the population
						Spiritual civilizations
	Death		at the end nourishment by Ki alone			
120 years	birth					

YANG DAY

YIN NIGHT

Table 8. Comparison of the evolution of man and of civilizations.

It has been remarked that this manifestation of the Universal Energy describes a centripetal logarithmic curve. There is a contraction in the time-scale.

The infinite universe is composed of galaxies of which our own forms one — the Milky Way. This is a spiral vortex of centripetal energy, of which the visible Yang part consists of planets and of stars spread across a diameter of 70,000 light years. To this is added all the invisible Yin energy, which creates the stars and planets untiringly by concentration.

Our solar system is one of millions of systems turning in centrepetal spirals round the centre of the galaxy, its orbit contracting slowly towards the centre. Since the movement is a spiral one, the centre is displaced a little to one side of the orbit. It follows that when the earth, which accompanies the sun, passes close to the centre, the climate is very hot and tropical (the secondary era) and that the climate becomes glacial when the earth moves further out. Hence one full revolution creates four seasons. The galactic year lasts 200 million solar years. We are going to take a look at life on earth during the galactic year now in progress. In the last galactic summer (our secondary era) the climate was very hot and plants and animals grew to giant size (Yin), as for example did the dinosaurs. Where such climatic conditions have been more or less preserved in our present equatorial and tropical zones, descendants of these species such as the elephants and every Yin fruit like bananas and oranges are still to be found.

When the galactic autumn arrives, the cold contracts all structures. Species become smaller and more active (Yang) and the gigantic species disappear. Then the earth continues its course. It is now far from the centre of the galaxy and winter has set in with widespread glaciation. Man appeared on the scene at the onset of winter some 25 million years ago in the tertiary period, and we are going to see why and where.

The Flow of Ki
The earth's axis is always turned towards the centre of the galaxy with the northern hemisphere on the outside and the south pole pointing towards the centre. This is a cosmic fact.

Because of this, the northern hemisphere is more Yang than
the southern hemisphere. There are more land masses in the
north (solidity is Yang) and more water in the south (liquidity
is Yin). In addition, the flow of Ki, which is directed from the
exterior to the centre of the galaxy, mainly strikes the
northern hemisphere; which is why spirituality is always
stronger there. In the galactic winter, the earth (which is
then well away from the centre) is subject to more of the
centripetal flow of Ki in its centrifugal motion (analogous to
the winter of the solar year and the night of the daily cycle).
This is why it is important to sleep with one's head to the
north and one's feet pointing to the centre of the galaxy. The
head is then always turned to the exterior of the galaxy and
receives the maximum flow of Ki. Now, it is well known that
the energy of heaven penetrates the crown of the head and
then flows from the head to the feet. By sleeping with one's
head to the north one increases the flow of Ki received,
while, at the same time, increasing the permeability of the
body to this flow. Having explained the cosmic situation of
the earth, let us now examine the characteristics of man.

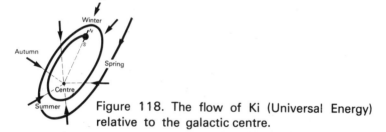

Figure 118. The flow of Ki (Universal Energy)
relative to the galactic centre.

The species of animal which once existed and now exist
on the earth represent all the possible combinations in which
the different chakras of the body can be arranged, from their
horizontal alignment in fish to their vertical alignment in
man.

Once these arrangements have been established, the
chakras receive the cosmic energy in accordance with the
geometry of the receptors, and this determines the
characteristics of each species. Thus, in yoga it is important
to adopt all these animal positions (which give their names
to the asanas) so that we can experience once again, the

great cosmic voyage of the species — just as we do as a developing embryo in our mother's womb. The positions are those of fish, reptiles, birds, mammals and finally man (watch the look on a child's face when at last he manages to stand up straight *by himself*). It may be understood, therefore, that the asanas should not be practised in any other order.

Thus man, the last to appear, and with his chakras aligned vertically towards the heaven above (a spiritual channel), arrived in winter, at an epoch of the greatest spirituality, and in the northern hemisphere, where spirituality is highest on earth. It is the northern hemisphere, too, where the great civilizations have developed in the past (to avoid any misunderstanding, let it be said that the earth's axis has turned over several times and this has brought about reversals of the poles and of the northern hemisphere).

Plant species also continued to evolve when the galactic winter came by becoming more concentrated (Yangization), due to the fact that the centripetal force of the flow of Ki had become greater. A many-chambered fruit, similar to the orange for example, had its sections reduced to two and then one, its rind hardened and turned dry and the fruit grew very small until we got the grains and cereals which made their appearance at the same times as man. They underwent and registered the same cosmic influences, which is why they are the ideal food for man. It is not by chance that their composition corresponds exactly to the composition of our blood.

Since they arrived last, they represent an evolved energy, whereas tropical fruits contain a fossil form of energy.

In Conclusion

Although we must end the book here, your investigation into the nature of the universe should continue. Remain aware, attentive and curious however old you become; there is no need to lose your youthfulness. Never forget the simple rule, the golden rule of health: *Be hungry every day* for this is a source of joy, of justice and of liberty.

INDEX

Learn How to Massage
W. Acramd. com
coconut oil
moisterase oil